BREEDING DAIRY CATTLE

To my eldest daughter,
Annalise

BREEDING DAIRY CATTLE

BY

DR JOHN HINKS

FARMING PRESS LIMITED
WHARFEDALE ROAD, IPSWICH, SUFFOLK, ENGLAND.

First published 1983
ISBN 0 85236 136 X

Made and printed in Great Britain by The Garden City Press Limited,
Letchworth, Hertfordshire SG6 1JS.

CONTENTS

Page

Chapter 1

INTRODUCTION

IN COMMON with every other human activity, agriculture in general and milk production in particular have not escaped the rigours and consequences of recent developments in technology. New knowledge and skills, facilities and resources—disseminated rapidly around the globe by improved methods of communication and transport—have created novel markets and food products, new production methods and ever-increasing competition. Social and political activity, accompanying and responding to the growth in technology, has brought about changes in consumer habits and demands, opened up new opportunities for trade, removed former constraints and introduced new ones.

For those whose function it is to anticipate and supply the needs of society for basic food products, the propagation of prime seed stock—an esoteric pursuit once regarded as offering secure, serene and lucrative part-time employment for the landed gentry and its youngest son—has become, in the space of a lifetime, a highly technical profession in which only the practitioner possessed of great knowledge and skill, stamina, versatility and good fortune can hope to survive and prosper. In the course of this rapid evolution, those who have proved unwilling or unable to adapt have been swept aside, rigorously and ruthlessly culled, along with all those whose misplaced or misguided enthusiasm has caused them to employ the failed technology, the inappropriate method or the inadequate material.

Though many relics of past tradition may remain to colour the cattle breeding scene and to divert and amuse the flippant and frivolous, the stockman dependent upon the dairy cow for his livelihood now recognises these as superficial and no longer accommodates them within his thinking and business planning. To such dedicated professionals within the farming community this text is respectfully addressed.

Fewer in number and owning greater resources than ever before, the current generation of milk producers is considerably more specialised and self-reliant than its predecessors, no longer farming several animal species in small mixed family enterprises. Whilst concentration on a single activity may offer considerable benefits of scale and provide added scope for professionalism to flourish, the successful dairy-businessman still needs to acquire mastery of many diverse skills. Regrettable as it may be to some, the day when prosperity could be achieved on the strength of excellence in a single discipline has departed, in the Developed World at least, possibly for ever.

To the extent that a mating, a conception, a gestation and a calving are indispensable features of the milk production process, all producers are perpetually faced with complex breeding decisions—firstly in the foundation of a herd and subsequently in its replacement and perpetuation. The achievement of an effective herd development and maintenance programme requires optimal solutions to three related questions—namely, when to act, which parental combinations to employ and which material to retain for future use. The degree of care and expertise brought to bear in solving these problems predetermines and conditions the capacity of the herd and the individual animal to respond to the management treatments imposed upon it and to exist in harmony with its environment.

Of the many treatments available to farmers and imposed by them on dairy herds, selective breeding alone offers lasting cumulative benefits extending across human and animal generations, yielding financial rewards and personal satisfaction comparable with those to be derived from the care and attention devoted to the preparation of a seedbed or to the health and fertility of the soil. Viewed as a science subject to the laws and theories of probability, cattle breeding extends the same challenges, the same fascinations and the same scope for expertise to flourish and rashness to bring its own rewards as the racetrack, the casino and the stock exchange.

For these many reasons, the breeding of the dairy herd has to occupy a prominent position in any scale of priorities relating to herd development and improvement. Anyone inclined to doubt this need pause only long enough to reflect upon the attributes of individuals and herds that have failed to compete and have departed the dairy cattle scene.

Only a fortunate few are able to achieve simultaneous mastery of several skills. For most of us, the pressures and complexities of daily life can be resisted and sustained only on the strength of technical advice and support supplied by others possessed of the time, imagination and opportunity needed to encompass broad perspectives, to visualise long-term horizons and to comprehend abstruse concepts and difficult principles.

Cattle breeding is no exception. Even today, the basic principles of animal genetics—the scientific discipline upon which modern breeding methods depend—are understood by only a small number of practitioners and advisers and applied by fewer still. In this particular area of farming activity the normal educational and instructional processes are demonstrably inadequate and the direct and indirect links between primary producer, local adviser and technical specialist tenuous and remote.

The most obvious and immediate consequence of ignorance and neglect is vulnerability to exploitation by the unscrupulous and avaricious, perhaps best exemplified in this case by the profiteering activities of the ever-present semen salesman and his embryo-peddling cousin. Until the time arrives when milk producers fully acknowledge the importance of selective breeding, not as a distinct subsidiary activity but rather as one of several herd treatments to be applied with the same ease and fluency as every other, the need for further education and specialised technical support will continue. If selective breeding still remains the most neglected area of herd development, then by the same token, it also remains the one activity offering further scope for dramatic advancement.

For this unsatisfactory situation the scientist and the professional development agencies are equally at fault. Concerned almost exclusively with animals maintained in controlled and hygienic laboratory conditions, or else with large animal populations which, once processed through a computer to remove the anomalies, tend to conform and respond to genetic manipulation in tidy predictable ways; lacking knowledge and first-hand experience of the specific problems that arise amongst small groups of animals at farmyard level and of the limitations imposed by impatient creditors, the professional animal geneticist is not well equipped to address himself to the problems encountered by the primary producer and has failed to supply the technical support and assistance needed. Amongst the many excellent and authoritative texts available to farmers and students on all aspects of animal management and behaviour, the simple practical guide to the genetic improvement of the dairy herd is conspicuous by its absence.

The task of remedying the deficiency is a daunting and formidable one, presenting obvious difficulties not only in communicating highly technical concepts in straightforward terms but also in bridging the credibility gap that has always separated the primary producer from the so-called 'technical expert'. In the present instance, these difficulties are exacerbated by exigencies of space which preclude treatment of some aspects of a very broad subject area and necessitate superficial treatment of others.

In the interests of simplicity, a conscious effort has been made to avoid the use of convenient but unnecessary jargon, though some inevitably remains to confuse and infuriate the reader. For similar reasons, technical explanations that are readily available from other sources or considered to be of less than vital importance in achieving an understanding of breeding principles and methods have been omitted (e.g. the processes by which the breeding value of a male or the genetic index of a female are calculated). Finally, many statements and assertions are made throughout the text in the belief that the time has arrived when these no longer need to be justified by supporting evidence (e.g. the advantages of AI, the merit of the proven sire and the unsatisfactory and misleading nature of lactation averages, selected records, dam–daughter comparisons and so on).

In conclusion, the central message it is hoped to convey to

the reader is one of encouragement. Despite the powerful and all-pervasive influence of those who, for personal profit or advancement, need or wish to confuse and cloud the scene and to convince their listeners otherwise, the breeding of a highly productive, profitable dairy herd remains essentially a straightforward matter, a science in which sustained success can be guaranteed provided that realistic objectives are set and a few basic guidelines and operational procedures are assiduously practised. That the science may be inexact, concerned with probabilities rather than black-and-white certainties, does not detract from this central fact and provides no justification for the admission of superstition, mythology and obscurantism. To the modern progressive dairy farmer-businessman, the 'master' breeder—supposedly possessed of occult skills, unique insights and a special understanding of cause and effect denied to lesser mortals—is as relevant and useful as the witch-doctor, astrologer or alchemist. If this text succeeds in achieving nothing more than to convince a single reader of this truth, it will have served a useful purpose.

Chapter 2

THE HISTORICAL BACKGROUND

AMIDST THE comfort and security of a modern welfare state, fully immersed in the present and anxious about the immediate future, it is all too easy for the busy working farmer to ignore or discount the importance to his business of the formative historical processes, directional evolutionary forces, random events and accidents that have predetermined today's realities and still condition future possibilities for further improvement.

Even within the highly developed systems of Western Europe the dairy herd unit of more than twenty cows is still the exception to the rule, the dominant Friesian breed still essentially mongrel by nature and the high-yielding dairy cow—sheltered from the elements in winter and waited upon by specialists in animal nutrition, health and reproduction—itself a novel and still remarkable phenomenon.

Table 1. World population and milk production—the challenge

Area	Population (million)	Total milk production per annum (million tonne)	Average milk yield per cow per annum (kg)
Western Europe	350 (8%)	150 (30%)	3,700
East Europe & USSR	400 (9%)	130 (25%)	2,300
North America	250 (6%)	70 (15%)	5,200
Elsewhere	175 (4%)	20 (5%)	3,500
Developed world	1,175 (27%)	370 (75%)	3,100
Developing world	3.300 (73%)	115 (25%)	655

Source: FAO Production Yearbook 1981.

Table 2. Global trends in milk production 1970–80

| Region | Total number of cattle | Dairy cattle numbers | Percentage change 1970–80 | | | |
			Annual milk yield/cow	Total milk production	Total cheese production	Total butter production
Denmark	+ 4	− 6	+19	+12	+95	− 15
France	+10	+ 4	+16	+21	+47	+ 10
W. Germany	+ 7	− 3	+18	+14	+56	+ 15
Italy	− 8	+ 8	+ 4	+13	+30	+ 5
Netherlands	+39	+25	+16	+44	+58	+ 52
United Kingdom	+ 6	0	+23	+23	+72	+167
Canada	− 1	−10	+22	+10	+60	+ 1
USA	+ 6	−13	+11	− 4	+72	− 32
W. Europe	+ 9	+ 3	+16	+20	+49	+ 24
N. America	+ 6	+ 3	+ 9	+13	+58	− 4
E. Europe & USSR	+ 9	+ 7	+ 5	+13	+49	+ 33
Australasia	+11	−24	+19	−10	+44	− 26
Developed world	+ 9	+ 2	+12	+14	+52	+ 15
Developing world	+11	+27	+ 8	+37	+27	+ 29
World	+10	+13	+ 4	+17	+48	+ 18

Source: FAO Production Yearbook 1981.

For the animal geneticist currently preoccupied with the development and introduction of increasingly sophisticated evaluation procedures not needed by industry and for the technologist now offering techniques of a potency that cannot be fully exploited, the observation that almost all of the genetic progress achieved so far has been accomplished within the last twenty-five years, mostly in the Developed World and almost entirely in response to straightforward processes of breed substitution is equally illuminating and sobering.

Historically, the bovine has been employed and exploited on occasion as a source of work, transport, clothing, medicine, sport, fuel, manure and religious symbol. Until quite recently its other function as a source of meat and dairy products for human consumption has tended to represent a useful, strictly seasonal, by-product usually but not always obtained once all other needs have been met. In peasant communities throughout vast regions of the globe the primitive functions of the species still retain an overwhelming importance. Massive stocks of unimproved indigenous cattle still await the removal of the major limiting factors that prevent the application of modern selective breeding measures. Even within the highly developed production systems of North America, Australasia and Western Europe the competing claims of the different functions of dairy cattle still confuse and complicate the specification of commercial objectives and the choice of materials and methods used to attain them.

OBJECTIVES IN ANIMAL BREEDING

Since prehistoric times Man's primary preoccupation and aim in animal husbandry may be viewed in terms of a relentless and unremitting campaign to eliminate wastage amongst his stock—firstly, by the removal or control of the more obvious sources of catastrophic loss caused by flood, tempest, pestilence, predator and famine and, subsequently, by removal or treatment of the chronic wastage associated with disease, infertility and constitutional weakness. Even today, animal survival and fitness tend to dominate all other considerations and priorities in dairy herd management. Rash and unprofitable as it may be to attempt to anticipate the future, the campaign to promote improved health, viability and fertility would seem likely to continue for as far ahead as anyone can reasonably envisage.

Subject to frequent setback by strife, conquest and natural disaster, any success that has been achieved in extending the useful lifespan of domesticated animals or in raising their fertility status has served to release additional animal and financial resources and to provide increased scope for other demands and preferences to emerge and be met. Each important step in the evolutionary process has been inextricably linked with changes and improvements in the human condition—in some instances, the animal benefitting from its human keeper and in others contributing to his improved status and wellbeing—to such an extent that it is now difficult to determine in many situations which of the two species has become the more dependent on the other. The highly productive, highly specialised dairy cattle enterprises of California, which probably represent the fullest expression of the stockman's achievements to date, still owe as large a debt to the efforts of Neanderthal and medieval herdsmen as to the highly publicised, prestigious and very recent inputs of the scientist and technologist.

For the greatest part of its history the bovine species has been subject to natural selection and—wherever and whenever possible—to the expression of human preference and prejudice in respect of the more visible external features of colour, texture, shape, size, form and behaviour. Ignorant of the laws and processes of inheritance and unaided by modern technology, the monks, nobility and gentry of medieval Europe manipulated and fashioned whatever material the local environment permitted to live, thrive and multiply, inducing profound changes in animal appearance and behaviour.

The combined efforts of natural and human selective agencies, operating from the time the species was first domesticated, has brought about the virtual elimination of genetic variation in fertility and animal fitness and supplied Bakewell (1725–95) and the pioneer breeders with the distinctive animal types that formed the foundation material for their early experiments in livestock improvement.

METHODS

The interval separating Bakewell from the present day may be regarded as a time spent in seeking to understand and explain the twin processes of evolution and inheritance and in establishing the massive, highly integrated infrastructure needed to implement and exploit the methodology he and his disciples proposed—the comprehensive registers of parentage, national milk recording schemes, centralised marketing structures, AI service networks and computing technology without which the ambitious improvement programmes now applied as a matter of routine in all developed countries could not possibly function. Despite all the time, effort and expense that has been invested in the search for quicker, cheaper, simpler and more effective procedures, the genetic improvement of dairy cattle in the final quarter of the twentieth century still rests almost exclusively upon a methodology first prescribed as appropriate in the final quarter of the eighteenth.

The legacy bequeathed by the innovators of the eighteenth and nineteenth centuries has not been exclusively beneficial. Whilst understandable and possibly unavoidable in the circumstances of the time, the high priority assigned by the early breeders to the purely external physical features of beauty and form have persisted through to the present day, manifest still in the presence of cattle fanciers, in the inordinate value still attached to show-ring success and in the proliferation of costly, extravagant and largely ineffective and counterproductive type classification schemes.

The failure on the part of breeders and specialists alike to devise and introduce measurement and descriptive procedures that clearly differentiate between the repeatable and transmissible components of functional and biological excellence on the one hand and the transient and misleading effects of stockmanship, preferential treatment and contrived cosmetic culling on the other has proved enormously costly in terms of misplaced and misdirected effort and continues to retard progress even today. In this connection the difficulties now experienced in calving heifers mated to a bull of their own breed—a problem that appears to have been exacerbated by earlier selection for type traits of dubious functional value—provides an excellent example of the case in point.

THE CONTRIBUTION OF CENTRALISED MARKETING ARRANGEMENTS

The establishment of centralised co-operative milk marketing schemes throughout Western Europe and the New World in the 1930s and 1940s constituted an historical turning point in the evolution of dairy farming, an innovation as momentous for the future development of cattle breeding activity as the technological revolution that immediately succeeded it.

For cattle breeding, centralised milk marketing and the accounting processes associated with it, though not recognised as being of significance in this particular connection at the time, have provided the platform upon which all subsequent developments and achievements have rested, including the introduction and further refinement of the technical processes themselves. In the absence of centrally controlled milk marketing, the long-term security, regularity of income and guaranteed degree of price stability needed to embark on costly and protracted enterprises of the kind necessary to induce continuous genetic progress in large breed populations and smaller herd units did not exist and could not have been established.

As it is, dairy farmers underpinned by their milk marketing organisations now enjoy a security and regularity of income that is not available in most other areas of farming activity and which fully compensates most of them for their involvement in what is frequently a demanding and unpleasant occupation. The basic and obvious distinction between stable milk markets on the one hand and the still chaotic and unpredictable meat markets on the other has several profound implications for the conduct of a dairy farmer's business enterprise, as will be seen later (Figure 1).

The very large business-orientated organisations that

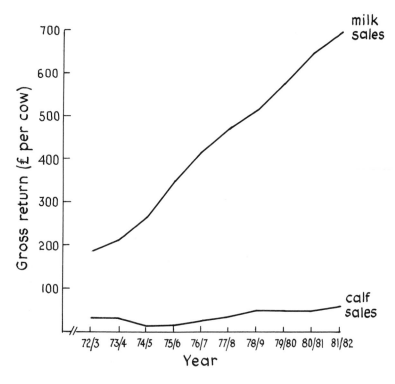

Fig. 1. Changes in the relationship between income derived from milk and calf sales 1972—82.

Source: Reports of the Breeding and Production Organisation of the Milk Marketing Board.

assumed initial responsibility for the marketing processes rapidly added other useful and important activities to their primary function, including that of representing the interests of their farmer-owners at the highest policy-making levels. In the conditions of the time, the marketing organisations represented the only institutions capable of accepting responsibility for the provision of the national milk recording, artificial insemination and documentation services needed to raise the dairy industry from its fragmented, vulnerable and demoralised state to the cohesive industrial entity it is today.

Table 3. The reproductive characteristics of species that predetermine breeding possibilities and choice of breeding methods

	Pig	Sheep	Dairy cow
Average productive lifespan (years)	3.0	3.5	3.7
Age at first mating (months)	8	18	18
Litters per annum	2.2	0.9	0.9
Offspring per litter	9.0	1.4	0.9
Productive sex	♂, ♀	♂, ♀	♀
Productive offspring per annum	20.0	1.3	0.4
Productive offspring—lifetime	60.0	4.5	1.5

The Contribution of Science and Technology

The disciplined and highly effective development processes devised and tested in laboratory samples and subsequently applied within the agricultural industry to bring about genetic change in the morphology, behaviour and yield characteristics of plants and the smaller species of farm animals have proved totally inappropriate for use with the larger species, as the protracted and costly Danish experience with central test stations has so vividly demonstrated.

The low fecundity, late sexual maturity and protracted lifespan of the dairy cow, together with her sheer physical size, high asset value and substantial replacement cost have precluded the adoption of the intensive centralised testing methods that are needed to achieve accuracy and diversity in selection and to minimise wastage of animal, human and technical resources. In dairy cattle, the inability—on the grounds of cost alone—to apply clinical design and experimental procedures in the testing and evaluation phase has excluded from the selective breeding process many attributes of interest and importance to dairy farmers and has necessitated the development of extensive testing and monitoring systems utilising whatever facilities and skills happen to be available on farms. At a time when plant, poultry and pig populations were already responding to the efforts of breeders, the achievement of even this compromise solution in dairy cattle had to await further structural changes and technical innovations.

The introduction of commercial AI services, initially for the modest purpose of providing a substitute for the costly and potentially dangerous farm bull as a means of getting cows with-calf, has been directly responsible for many other profound and lasting developments, few of which could possibly have been foreseen at the outset and several of which have still to be fully recognised and exploited.

The technical breakthrough in reproductive technology which made it possible to transfer a laboratory technique directly to the farmyard and cattleshed, together with the progeny testing procedure with which AI rapidly became inextricably linked, have been jointly responsible for the creation of a unique product—the AI-proven sire—that has played a dominant and still only partially-fulfilled role in shaping and perpetuating the present world dairy cattle scene and in opening up even brighter prospects for future advancement. Of considerable importance in its own right and also in terms of the many consequences it has engendered on the farm and in the general community, each contribution made by the proven bull deserves to be identified and given further consideration:

- The virtual disappearance of the stock service bull—a commodity of unknown or dubious genetic merit—from dairy farms.
- The almost complete eradication of venereal disease and control of genetic abnormalities to such an extent that these particular benefits, still of substantial value to the industry, are now taken for granted and no longer credited to their primary source.
- The demonstration in many twin trials and animal transfer studies of the truism that genetic excellence is not confined to the fashionable herds of a small number of 'master' breeders but is more likely to be found elsewhere in more obscure sectors of animal populations.
- The transfer of immediate responsibility for the most influential breeding and selection decisions away from the farming community to the specialists and bureaucrats, with

all that this implies in terms of central controls, restrictive practices, lack of knowledge and sympathy for the local scene and the imposition of compromise solutions based on the lowest common level of interest and need.

- The elevation of the male sex to a dominant role in the breeding process which, together with the technical ability to transfer gametes rapidly and at low cost over long distances, has diminished genetic variation between previously isolated animal populations, destroyed the concept of national autonomy in cattle breeding and now promises to open up novel opportunities for the introduction of fully integrated breeding programmes at intercontinental and global levels.
- The elevation of cattle breeding from its lowly status as a localised village pastime to that of a fully-fledged international industry of massive proportions.

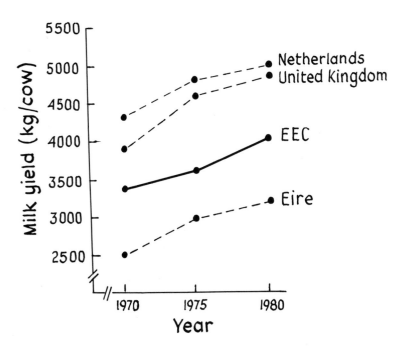

Fig. 2. Trends in milk production—yield per cow.

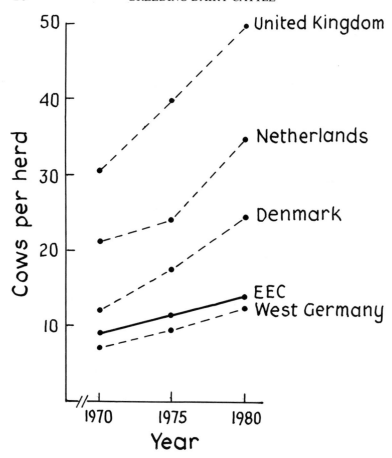

Fig. 3. Trends in milk production—average herd size.

- The promotion of breeds possessing the numerical strength needed to supply the exorbitant demands of the progeny test procedure for very large numbers of milk recorded animals to the detriment and virtual exclusion of all other breeds lacking this particular advantage.
- The propagation of animal stocks which, now possessed of a very high intrinsic potential for milk production, are less flexible than their predecessors in their capacity to respond to changes in social, political and financial circumstances.

- The promotion of specialisation at the expense of diversification.

The application of technology to cattle breeding has led to some unforeseen and intriguing consequences that pose fascinating questions for the future. The improved stock produced by the pioneer breeders not only graced their immediate locality but spread far afield to populate new environments in the New World. Following a period of consolidation and refinement in partial or total isolation from the parental stock, selected descendants are now returning to Western Europe in ever-increasing numbers to reinvigorate the degenerate ancestral material.

Whether this process will continue for long into the future or whether the flow will again be reversed depends on many unknown factors, not least upon the ability of cattle breeders in North America to resist the complacency that success inevitably induces, and upon the ability of their European counterparts to seize and fully exploit the temporary advantages gained by the importation of superior stock from their competitors.

Chapter 3

SPECIFICATION OF OBJECTIVES

EFFECTIVE BUSINESS planning entails a clear understanding of precisely where one wishes to go, where one stands at present and how best to attain the former status from the latter. This, in turn, calls for a clear statement of aims and goals—both long-term and short-term—an objective specification of the present state of the enterprise and a detailed knowledge of the various alternative treatments available and the efficacy of each.

Whilst external events that cannot always be anticipated and allowed for may intervene to prevent a planned programme from achieving the most profitable end result, a common failing in long-term herd programming can be identified and precluded from the start. The tendency of many breeders to seek to achieve what may be desirable at the expense of what is attainable diminishes prospects of success from the very beginning and must be firmly resisted by anyone determined to exclude all avoidable sources of inefficiency.

The first, and possibly the most important and difficult step in establishing an effective herd improvement scheme is the achievement of a clear and unequivocal statement of long- and short-term herd objectives and of the strategy and tactics to be employed in seeking to attain them.

Any forward planning and budgeting exercise of this kind intended to identify and exploit to best advantage all the opportunities the market place presents must first acknowledge and accommodate the fundamental and inescapable principle that the more numerous and diverse the objectives, the slower and lesser will be the progress achieved towards each and the greater the risk of partial or total failure (see Figure 11 and Table 6). Whilst the high risks incurred in attempting to pursue single objectives are recognised by most businessmen and detract from the virtues of extreme specialisation, the inevitable loss of efficiency and the dissipation of skill and effort associated with extreme diversification, though less obvious, are equally real and can prove just as costly in the long run.

The unique characteristics of milk production introduced by price control mechanisms and specialised marketing arrangements should not be allowed to obscure the fact that the dairy farming business is subject to the same basic rules, influences and constraints that obtain in general industrial practice. The prospects of a dramatic success or an equally dramatic failure tend to reflect not only the competence of the farmer himself but also his willingness to accept risk. The values of products tend to reflect their scarcity as well as their quality (e.g. the asset value of a show-winning cow or a fashionable pedigree herd). Herd responses to treatments applied by the farmer tend to display the same diminishing-return syndrome that characterises most business enterprises. In the present context the perennial dilemma facing all investors—whether and when to realise an immediate profit at the expense of long-term growth in capital assets—is particularly relevant in affecting the choice between treatments and particularly acute in small businesses operating on borrowed capital.

The profitability of a dairy herd is determined by a complex input–output relationship in which the sources of revenue are usually few in number and easy to identify—namely, milk, the surplus calf and the cull cow. The inputs on the other hand are many and varied and not always obvious either in their own right or in terms of their influence on other inputs and outputs.

Whilst self-evident, the argument that profit maximisation is achieved by minimising costs and maximising revenues does not provide any answers for producers puzzled as to whether to opt for an intensive high-output/high-cost system, an extensive low-cost system or some intermediate form.

In the event, most producers in recent years—including those operating a low-cost system—have sought to maintain profit margins by increased productivity whilst also attempting to achieve a balance between their long- and short-term interests and between their various sources of income. Given present uncertainties about future trading conditions there are no grounds for supposing these decisions to have been misplaced, despite the problems and embarrassments production surpluses may present to those responsible for the marketing processes.

FACTORS AFFECTING CHOICE OF TREATMENT

1. Time Horizons

Selective breeding is only one of many treatments available to farmers wishing to influence and improve the performance of their dairy cattle enterprise. Whilst not necessarily more important or more valuable to the practitioner, the responses induced by attention paid to nutrition, medication, hygiene, housing and the use of labour and equipment are often dramatic, immediate and highly visible. By contrast, herd and animal responses to the mating and breeding process are usually slow to reveal themselves, less conspicuous when they do and are essentially long-term in nature—characteristics that tend to deter all those with short-term horizons in view and to cause most to underestimate and undervalue the contribution itself. The time-worn arguments of animal geneticists to the effect that selection responses are inexpensively obtained, cumulative across successive genera-tions and of astronomical monetary value when summated across the large numbers of animals benefiting from them, whilst undoubtedly valid, are not easy to demonstrate convincingly outside the controlled and highly artificial conditions of the research laboratory or experimental station.

Whilst heavy culling and the facility to move outside the confines of the herd at any time to introduce purchased stock may evoke rapid and detectable changes in the appearance and performance attributes of a herd, the routine day-to-day mating and replacement decisions being taken now do not begin to influence the milking section of the herd until some three to four years hence. Once introduced, these influences—whether beneficial or detrimental—may remain in the offspring to condition the business for some fifteen to

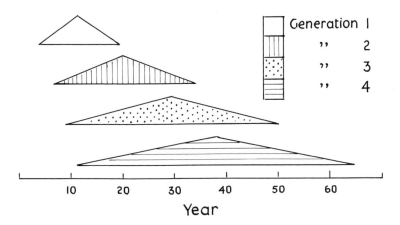

Fig. 4. Time scales in herd maintenance and replacement illustrating the overlap between successive animal generations.

twenty years to come, up to the point at which the final surviving daughter reaches the end of her productive lifespan. In the case of some attributes and some individual sires and dams, the influence of a mating decision taken today may still be detectable in the second, third and fourth-generation descendants some thirty to fifty years after the initial event (see Figure 4). Against such a protracted timetable of events, the working lifetime of a dairy farmer is not a long one.

Consequently, the breeding of the dairy herd has to be viewed in strategic rather than tactical terms, in precisely the same light as other major capital undertakings that increase the asset value of the holding and offer large but delayed returns on invested capital (e.g. land reclamation, shelter-belt provision). In such circumstances, it is of supreme importance that the targets and objectives of the exercise are themselves highly robust and insensitive to short-term changes in priorities.

Accepting the argument that market conditions to change in the short term and that new opportunities of short duration do arise from time to time and must, if possible, be fully exploited whenever they do, the long-term herd development strategy must also be sufficiently flexible to accommodate and respond to them and the farmer himself fully alert as to the kind of changes in policy and direction that can and cannot be introduced without causing lasting or serious damage to his development plans. In this respect, examples of herds in which many years of accumulated progress have been sacrificed overnight on grounds of expediency, or in which the benefits derived from the application of one treatment have been entirely negated by the hasty introduction of others, are not difficult to find.

Assuming profit maximisation to be the most important single objective of most practising dairy farmers, the multiple aims of a fully integrated herd development programme may be categorised—for purposes of convenience only—under the following broad headings:

Productivity
Fertility
Health
Constitutional soundness
Behaviour
Longevity.

Whilst each of these aspects may be considered important in its own right, the list is not exhaustive and its components are clearly not mutually exclusive. Thus good health is implicit in the achievement of high productivity and fertility in the achievement of a long lifespan. Nevertheless, within these crudely defined headings it is possible to begin to identify the kind of specific planning objective that is likely to prove relatively insensitive to changing priorities and which is thus, by definition, appropriate for manipulation by selective breeding or other long-term treatments.

For example, having identified optimal fertility as a general, desirable long-term objective, it is reasonable to proceed to the next stage and to pinpoint the attainment of a 365-day herd calving interval as a more specific and well-defined target which is desirable and profitable in its own right and likely to remain so for the foreseeable future irrespective of short-term fluctuations in trading or political conditions. On the other hand, the achievement of a 4 per cent fat average, whilst possibly contributing to improvements in immediate revenues from milk sales, constitutes a target that is likely to remain desirable and profitable only for as long as current market priorities continue to prevail.

By processes of elimination, testing each major objective and component in turn for its sensitivity to time trends, it is possible to discriminate between those objectives and animal attributes that are both important in their own right and also relatively insensitive to change and thereby suitable for genetic treatment—as judged by this criterion at least—from those that lack guarantees of long-term stability and are clearly not appropriate for inclusion in long-term development strategies. Unfortunately, not all attributes of interest fall neatly and exclusively into one category or the other. At this point, expert advice is essential in order to determine the implications and possible consequences of a decision to include or exclude the particular objective in question.

2. Documentation Processes

The numbers of dairy farmers failing to assign the breeding process its correct status in the choice of treatments applied to their herds is matched by all those who consider selective breeding to offer a cure for all ills. Of the desirable, important and stable long-term objectives only some can be attained by selective breeding methods. A decision to apply selection as a preferred alternative to other long-term treatments or to reinforce them inevitably introduces several other presuppositions, all of which must be fully valid if the treatment is to be effective.

First—and perhaps most important of all—the attribute in question must be amenable to precise definition in meaningful biological terms and also to objective and unequivocal measurement at realistic cost—requirements that present breeders with immediate difficulties in respect of the documentation of most diseases, reproduction and fertility, food intake, conversion efficiency and appetite, longevity, behaviour and daughter type.

This particular obstacle standing in the way of already severely circumscribed possibilities for achieving genetic change is further exacerbated by the need to characterise animals sufficiently early in life to permit effective selection to be applied. In situations in which the young animal provides few useful clues as to its strengths and weaknesses later in life, late-developing conditions (e.g. early senile decay) cannot be controlled effectively by any genetic treatment applied within the herd itself. This important consideration fully explains and fully justifies the heavy emphasis placed upon first lactation performance in sire proving and indicates the intrinsic futility of several current practices that seek to retrieve irretrievable situations by genetic means (e.g. the type scoring of mature cows, use of mature records in sire testing).

Consequently, despite all the research and development time and effort invested in attempts to devise elaborate procedures by which to incorporate health, fertility and factors contributing to increased longevity within herd selection programmes, and despite many past claims to have achieved success in doing so, it remains as true today as ever before that only the simplest and most obvious aspects of animal productivity—essentially milk yield and its constituents together with the measurable growth and carcase characteristics—are eminently suitable for development by selective breeding. However important and desirable ease and regularity of calving and rebreeding, good health and a sound constitution, a placid temperament and a voracious appetite may be in determining the wellbeing of a dairy cattle enterprise, their inclusion amongst the selection criteria applied by farmers can only serve to further diminish an already limited scope for genetic improvement in the primary production traits.

For all those who may be inclined to discount the value and importance of selective breeding on the strength of these arguments and for all those inclined to support the plausible thesis that further improvement in the productive potential of dairy cows is no longer desirable at a time of surplus production, it suffices to point out that an increased genetic potential in this direction need not be utilised to increase total output. The same intrinsic potential may be exploited usefully to achieve fixed production targets with fewer animals and lower maintenance costs than before.

Having specified those aspects of productivity that can be measured simply, objectively and cheaply early in life as being the only attributes possessed of the proven capacity to respond clearly, unequivocally and in a controlled and predictable fashion to selective breeding, it remains to identify the specific components of productivity that exhibit a sufficient degree of genetic variation to warrant inclusion in the herd selection programme.

3. The Nature of Products

For a number of reasons, mainly historical, dairy farmers located in the New World have tended to distinguish between the milk and meat functions of dairy cattle much more clearly and decisively than their European counterparts, directing their businesses almost exclusively towards the maximisation of the dairy product. For them, the added complexities and agonising decisions that perpetually arise in attempting to reconcile and optimise two frequently conflicting objectives simply do not exist. In such circumstances, the wastage of surplus animals—the male calves and cull cows—which specialised units cannot accommodate and which are considered to have little other commercial value, is compensated by the preferential terms of trading, efficient use of capital and other resources and availability of special local advantages which tend to characterise the specialised unit.

In many parts of northern and western Europe, however, milk producers farming small units cannot afford to ignore the additional income to be derived from the cull cow and surplus calf. Consequently, owners of small herds, to whom the problem presents itself in its most direct and acute form, are obliged to seek a clear and rational solution before committing themselves to any development programme of a long-term nature.

The decision taken by all those European dairy farmers who have chosen to follow the North American example and specialise in milk production has much to commend it, if only in terms of consistency and singularity of purpose and regularity and security of income. Whilst this entirely pragmatic and self-interested justification for a major policy decision may not commend itself to national and international planners of food supplies or to other sectors of the livestock industry that traditionally depend on the dairy farmer to supply their raw materials, in the absence of price stability and guaranteed markets for surplus animals the incentive to specialise in milk production must remain very strong.

Given present disparities between the two sources of income (Figure 1) the 'single purpose—dual result' concept that has coloured the thinking and behaviour of European producers for so long lacks conviction and logic and, in common with many other compromise solutions adopted in response to uncertainty, introduces a real risk of failure to achieve sustained progress in either direction.

Accordingly, with the possible exception of a small number of producers particularly favoured by unusual local circumstances of the kind that engender long-term contracts at preferential prices for animals of an agreed specification, specialisation has to be commended as a preferred alternative to diversification for anyone seriously concerned with long-term herd development.

CHOICE OF PRODUCTION SYSTEM

On commencing milk production and on various occasions thereafter every dairy farmer has to address himself to the problem of choosing between an intensive high-cost, high-output system, an extensive low-cost system or some less extreme intermediate form.

Whilst the presence of large product surpluses throughout the Developed World and competition between animals and humanity for access to grain would appear to support the argument for self-sufficient production systems based mainly on grass, in the absence of quotas and other supply management mechanisms most producers have chosen to maintain profits by increasing scale, turnover and individual animal yields, compensating for a lower profit margin on each unit of production by producing more units. This policy decision, crucial in determining breed choice, herd calving and production patterns, building layout and design and so on, would seem to be justified by results if the characteristics of herds ceasing milk production provide any guidelines.

It is a matter of good fortune that the type of production system adopted, which clearly influences breed choice, does not appear to influence the type of animal within a breed that is most appropriate for a chosen system (see Table 9). All the evidence available from twin studies and breed comparisons seems to indicate that the animal that thrives within one system of management tends to prosper over a wide range of systems (Figure 21). Whilst this truism may not apply to extremes as large as those distinguishing the temperate regions from the tropics, for example, it does appear to hold good for systems as far apart as California, Australasia and northern Europe. Consequently, the question of management system, however complex and crucial for the individual producer, no longer figures prominently amongst the factors influencing the choice of appropriate methods and materials.

Chapter 4

FACTORS DETERMINING GENETIC RESPONSES TO SELECTIVE BREEDING

REDUCED TO barest essentials, the breeding and maintenance of a genetically superior dairy herd constitutes nothing
more than an exercise in mating the best males available to
the best females present in the herd and thereafter
substituting offspring for parents at the most appropriate
time. To this process two sexes of parents and two sexes of
offspring contribute, thereby affording four possible
pathways along which to promote genetic improvement.

Whilst matings are necessary to perpetuate the herd and to
initiate the sequence of events leading up to lactation, and
disposal and replacement processes cannot be dispensed with
if the surplus reproductive capacity of the herd is to be
contained within bounds, discrimination between animals on
grounds of genetic merit does not *have* to be exercised in
either case. However, both processes obviously permit the
introduction of selective preferences, in either sex or both, a
facility which farmers exploit to a greater or lesser extent for a
variety of purposes. Since the priorities and techniques may
differ when applying selection amongst sires and dams and
also in the breeding of sons and daughters, and further
opportunities exist to manipulate the timing of events,
considerable scope is available for skilled practitioners to
exploit the process to actively promote genetic excellence and
for the neglectful and incompetent to perpetuate mediocrity.

Of the several pathways through which the genetic
constitution of forthcoming generations may be influenced
and modified, only the processes by which their own females
are mated and subsequently replaced are of interest and

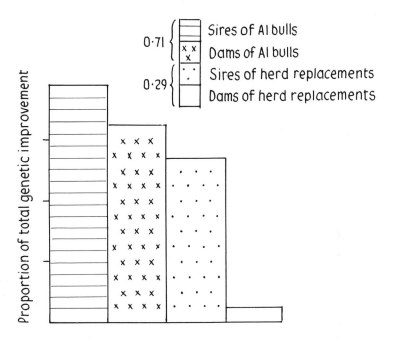

Fig. 5. Genetic responses to selection amongst the sires and dams of sons and daughters.

immediate concern to most dairy farmers and available to them as a means by which to exert a direct personal influence on future events. Despite the fact that most farmers contribute little to the processes that account for most of the genetic change occurring in dairy cattle populations (i.e. the matings, testing programmes and selection decisions that culminate in the appearance of proven bulls in AI studs), their own efforts in determining which particular proven bulls are used and which particular cows are employed to propagate the next generation of female replacements can add substantially to the rate and magnitude of genetic change within their own herds.

Even in the absence of any deliberate selection amongst animals on genetic grounds, some genetic change in animal populations and herds occurs naturally in response to sampling and other random events. These effects, particularly

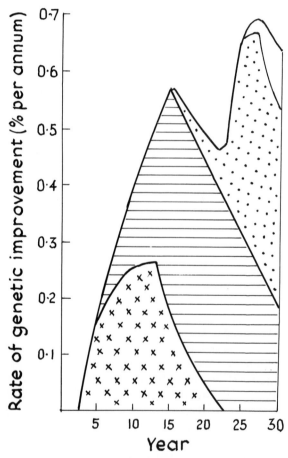

Fig. 6. Accumulation of genetic responses in successive
generations.

noticeable at herd level when they emerge in the form of colour variants or lethal and sub-lethal genetic abnormalities, tend to be unpredictable and, in the majority of cases, undesirable and detrimental. When superimposed on these seemingly haphazard events, preferential selection induces organised, directional change of a kind that causes each successive generation to excel or surpass its predecessor in the important and desirable traits.

Selective breeding differs profoundly from most other treatments applied to dairy herds and compares unfavourably with them by virtue of the long time-lag intervening between the initial matings and the first expression of genetic responses in the offspring—a time interval of some three to four years in the case of dams and daughters (see Figure 7). Nevertheless, this prolonged action–reaction time is fully compensated by an advantage unique to the breeding process, namely the retention and accumulation of genetic responses in successive generations (Figure 6). Whereas the changes introduced by most other treatments confer benefits only for as long as the treatment continues and frequently entail heavy capital investment and depreciation, any change induced by selection contributes to an appreciating capital asset and remains within the population thereafter, conferring lasting benefits in the absence of counter-selection.

In the simplest case, in which selection is directed exclusively towards the improvement of a single trait, the magnitude of the genetic response obtained in the next generation is determined by:

(a) the amount of variation present—i.e. the scale of differences separating the best individuals from the worst;

(b) the intensity of the selection process or amount of selection pressure applied;

(c) the heritability of the trait in question—a value which, at one and the same time, expresses the extent to which observed differences between individuals are transmitted between generations and also the accuracy with which the breeding value of an individual can be identified from its performance records or outward appearance;

(d) the number of offspring produced.

Of the factors determining genetic changes between successive generations, (a) and (b) jointly specify the observed superiority of the selected group of parents, (a) and (c) the amount of genetic variation available, (c) the proportion of parental superiority expected to re-emerge amongst the offspring prior to any further selection amongst them, and (d) the extent to which the genetic superiority of selected parents is disseminated throughout the population in the next generation.

From the viewpoint of the farmer seeking to breed superior female replacements, any mating or any parent of either sex that engenders only male calves or female calves that fail to gain entry to the milking herd has to be designated as being genetically 'dead' or inert in terms of its contribution to the next generation, regardless of its excellence in every other respect. Similarly, parental combinations that contribute several offspring to the milking herd may prove more influential in the long term than more outstanding combinations supplying fewer descendants.

Since each determinant of genetic change may vary according to the parental sex involved, the estimation or prediction of genetic responses to selection has to be conducted independently amongst sires and dams and the expected genetic superiority of the offspring derived as the mean of the responses obtained from each parental source.

In the context of selection within dairy herds, the greater intensity of selection that can be applied amongst male parents, the greater accuracy with which their breeding value can be estimated and the larger number of female offspring they are able to contribute to the next generation have combined to create a situation in which the male contribution to genetic change between generations is potentially very much greater—by a factor of eight to ten—than that of the female sex (see Figure 5). Thus, despite all the improvements in dairy cattle reproduction accomplished by AI and now promised by embryo transfer and other related techniques, the low fecundity and protracted lifespan of the typical dairy cow still remains the most important single obstacle to rapid genetic advancement in the dairy herd.

Unfortunately, this grossly oversimplified and idealised account of the basic processes by which genetic change is accomplished in dairy herds will not suffice to fully explain all the genetic events that are seen to occur within herds or to reveal the various influences that breeders are able to bring to bear. Small samples of parents and offspring, of the dimensions encountered at herd level, rarely behave in the same tidy and predictable manner as large populations and selection is only occasionally applied for a single attribute. Further, dairy cattle generations are not discrete, as they tend to be in plants, poultry and pigs, but overlap and mingle to an extent that permits parents and grandparents to compete for survival alongside daughters and granddaughters, further complicating the pattern of responses (Figure 7). Finally, the influence of time and monetary considerations, which has been ignored until now but which produces painful conflicts of interest between immediate profits and long-term capital appreciation, has to be introduced and allowed for.

DETERMINANTS OF GENETIC CHANGE

1. Variation

Amongst the effects generated by the host of causative factors responsible for differences between individual animals, the influence of underlying genetic activity may be witnessed immediately and unequivocally in the colour variants, horned and polled conditions and gross structural abnormalities that appear from time to time in response to the presence or absence of a *single gene*.

The most obvious and influential example of genetic differentiation at work may be observed as a matter of normal daily routine in the birth of two distinct sexes—a vital discriminatory event occurring at point of conception which, in response to the particular form in which a small sex chromosome is present in cells, dictates the function and form of an animal throughout its entire existence, severely constraining all future possibilities for genetic manipulation.

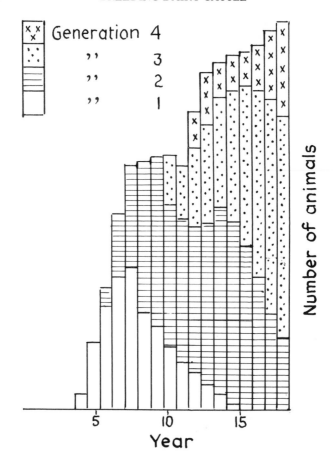

Fig. 7. Time-lags in herd improvement.

Whilst the facility to predetermine the sex of offspring may not yet be available, very large discontinuous, all-or-none, variation of this kind tends to make for simple and precise choices between animals, choices uncomplicated by the presence of intermediate types.

Discontinuous variation of a quite different kind is observed in some other characteristics—e.g. twinning. In these instances, which to all outward appearance are indistinguishable from the large all-or-none single gene

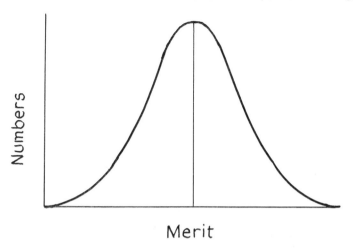

Fig. 8. The Normal Distribution.

effects, an accumulation of many genes, each exerting a small individual effect, eventually provokes an unexpected and dramatic response by the animal, culminating in the birth of twins or triplets in place of the customary singleton. Selective breeding for attributes of this special kind, in which the breaching of an underlying genetic barrier or threshold evokes a massive response, calls for the application of specialised knowledge and techniques. However, the traits that exhibit this unusual form of behaviour are few in number and normally of little immediate practical relevance and importance to farmers.

Most traits of interest and concern within dairy herds are controlled by many genes and display a characteristic pattern of continuous or quantitative variation that is usually depicted in the form of the familiar 'Normal Distribution' (Figure 8). This possesses statistical properties that are known and widely utilised by geneticists to predict and compare the probable effects of different selection procedures on populations subject to selective breeding.

Continuous variation of this kind arises in response to the combined influence of *all* the environmental factors—both positive and negative—that cause animals to differ amongst themselves, together with the effects of any genes that may influence the trait. In these circumstances, the *apparent* superiority of selected stock depends firstly upon the total amount of variation present (which determines the extent to which it is possible for individuals to deviate from average) and, secondly, upon the numbers of animals selected (which determines the extent to which they actually do exceed the average).

An ability to detect differences between animals and to set aside groups of individuals that exhibit an apparent superiority provides no assurance whatever that a trait will respond favourably or effectively to selective breeding. To the extent that non-genetic influences tend to dominate and distort the influence of all other factors, offspring may exhibit no discernible genetic response even to intense selection applied amongst parents that may appear to differ markedly in intrinsic merit (e.g. variation in the conception rate of females).

Numerous studies of parent–offspring and other family relationships have established that only some of the important animal attributes of interest to farmers are transmitted between generations to an extent sufficient to permit the recognition of genetic differences between individuals and to justify their exploitation within a dairy herd (Table 4).

The ability of a characteristic to respond effectively to

Table 4. The heritability of the major components of dairy cattle productivity and behaviour

	Heritability
Weight of milk, fat, solids	0.20–0.40
Fat %, protein %, solids %	0.35–0.55
Milking speed	0.20–0.30
Temperament	0.05–0.15
Reproductive failure	0.05–0.10
Mastitis susceptibility	0.05–0.15
Type score	0.10–0.25
Length of productive life	0.05–0.10

selection is measured and communicated in terms of its heritability value—a quantity which expresses the proportion of the apparent parental superiority expected to reappear in the next generation. In using and interpreting heritability estimates the customary cautionary note has to be sounded. Heritability values are usually derived from large population studies and may not fully apply when used in relation to small herd samples or when applied to management systems that differ markedly from those from which the estimates were initially obtained.

Since the heritability value constitutes a proportion of all variation arising from both genetic and non-genetic sources, it follows that any procedure that serves to reduce the non-genetic component must inflate the heritable component and thereby render the recognition of genetic merit easier and more precise. In practice, this result is achieved by standardising environments and management systems wherever possible in order to remove special treatment effects (e.g. as in the Danish test stations) by statistical adjustment of performance records to remove or minimise the influence of known sources of non-genetic variation (e.g. the truncation of lactation records to a standard 305-day value) and by the adoption of experimental design procedures (e.g. the planned distribution of semen to ensure a balanced progeny test result).

In their selection and use of males, farmers are able to exert a considerable influence on the accuracy, predictability and stability of their own herd development programmes. For those utilising AI, a considerable freedom of choice and action is available. Since the estimated breeding value of bulls proven on as few as thirty effective daughters in several herds provides a reliable indication of their true genetic merit—at least in respect of daughter productivity (Figure 9)—and large numbers of bulls of this kind are available at any time through AI, there seems to be no obvious justification for employing anything other than the fully proven AI-tested bull on cows intended to breed herd replacements. This uncompromising conclusion emerges not because all AI-proven sires are necessarily genetically superior to all others, but simply because the use of less well proven bulls

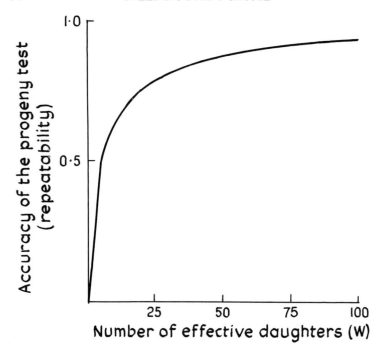

Fig. 9. The effect of variation in the number of effective daughters contributing to a sire proof on the accuracy (repeatability) of the text result.

inevitably introduces additional risk and uncertainty that need not be incurred.

In contrast to the males, remarkably little scope exists for the individual to exert a major influence on the accuracy of the female selection process. Despite the very considerable variation observed amongst milking cows in dairy herds, a number of biological constraints entirely beyond the control of the farmer impose severe upper limits on the exploitation of maternal superiority. In all herds, the low fecundity of the dairy cow and the depredation caused by natural wastage erodes most of the limited scope initially available for selection. Recently developed aids to female selection, including highly sophisticated index procedures, do not resolve this fundamental difficulty but may assist marginally by removing some of the inappropriate allowances and prejudices that many breeders tend to admit when deciding which particular animals to retain and discard.

2. Selection Intensity

The relationship between the numbers of parents actually used to breed herd replacements and the numbers potentially available for the purpose exerts a crucial influence on the magnitude of genetic change between generations. Clearly, the superiority of selected parents must be greater in situations in which small numbers are chosen from a large initial pool as opposed to circumstances in which most of the candidates have to be retained. In practice, the number of parents contributing to the next generation can only be determined after the event since all those that fail to breed daughters that subsequently gain entry to the milking herd must be counted as being genetically inert or sterile.

Genetic responses to changes in the proportion selected are not linear (Figure 10) and only assume major dimensions when the numbers potentially available for selection are very large. Whilst farmers are able to intensify female selection marginally by minimising all wastage—including misplaced selection for unimportant or inappropriate traits—the opportunity to modify the intensity of the parental selection process as a whole is, once again, confined essentially to the male sex. Even in herds in which every effort is made to maximise opportunities for female selection, at least 60 per cent of the entire female resource has to be retained from year to year. The superior tested males used at the same time represent one or two survivors of several thousand initial candidates.

The potentially large genetic response to be obtained by full exploitation of the opportunities presented by the male sex tend to be of a 'once-and-for-all' nature. Farmers adopting AI and nominating outstanding proven bulls for the first time can expect to observe a dramatic immediate response as soon as the offspring penetrate the herd and begin to displace the daughters of natural service bulls (see Figures 6 and 7). Thereafter, the same intensity of selection must be maintained amongst the males if the improved genetic status

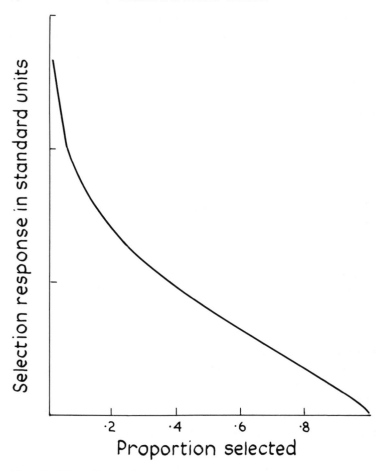

Fig. 10. The effect of variation in the proportion selected for breeding on the magnitude of genetic responses.

of the herd is to be sustained and slippage back to former levels prevented.

3. Generation Turnover
The time taken to replace one generation by its successor determines the speed with which genetic change occurs in dairy herds and is almost totally determined by the farmer

himself. In circumstances in which offspring are expected to excel parents in genetic merit, a very rapid replacement programme would seem to be called for and is essential if genetic progress is to be maximised. However, other important considerations intrude at this point to complicate an apparently straightforward issue and preclude easy general solutions and recommendations.

In the first place, time factors which directly influence the magnitude of genetic responses as well as the speed with which they are introduced provoke immediate conflicts of interest. The very high priority that cattle breeders assign to selection accuracy—which, in turn, reflects the high asset value and replacement cost of the animal—can usually be attained only by postponing the selection processes in order to procure the time needed to acquire additional records. Further, the protracted rearing phase and the high maintenance cost of dairy animals necessitate the retention of most of them for the length of time needed to recover initial investments and realise a profit.

The clash of interest between the wish to obtain a profit from the older cows and to turn generations over rapidly can only be resolved by compromise. Since the optimal solution in any single instance is highly sensitive to many local and temporal events, including the fluctuating status of local markets, no general solution can be prescribed. In the event, the only guidance that can be proferred is that of pointing out the truism that most actions that generate an immediate profit tend also to carry with them an unseen cost in terms of squandered future opportunities.

The irreconcilable problems presented by the female sex in respect of generation replacement do not arise in such acute form in the males. Whereas the consistent and widespread use of young bulls in place of the senior tested bulls may offer scope to hasten the turnover of generations, the loss of accuracy and added risks incurred in using them render them unacceptable to anyone wishing to promote herd stability. Provided that the proven bulls are replaced as soon as superior substitutes become available, their age would not seem to constitute a major limiting factor in dairy herd improvement.

SIMULTANEOUS SELECTION FOR SEVERAL ATTRIBUTES

Up to this point, genetic change between successive generations has been examined and explained in terms of the behaviour of a single trait. The application of simultaneous selection for several attributes immediately introduces problems of two distinct kinds—those connected with the determination of priorities and the partition of limited resources and others arising from the observation that animal traits are only occasionally genetically independent. Interference by the breeder in respect of any one trait tends to evoke a chain of sympathetic or antagonistic reactions elsewhere. In deciding which specific qualities to select for, the possibility of evoking indirect responses in many other directions has to be anticipated and allowed for.

In the simplest case, in which the traits are genetically discrete and the animal resources available for selection are predetermined, the inclusion of a second characteristic inevitably diminishes the amount of selection pressure that can be applied to the primary trait (Figure 11).

The effect of adding attributes to a selection portfolio is multiplicative rather than additive, as can be shown by means of simple arithmetical examples. Supposing, for example, that selection standards are established whereby individuals are required merely to exceed average in order to qualify for retention, then one animal in every two would be expected to qualify in respect of a single trait. Where two traits are included, the numbers likely to qualify on *both* counts are reduced to 1 in 4. Where higher qualifying standards are set, such that only the leading 25 per cent are approved for selection, the numbers qualifying on *all* counts are reduced to 1 in 4, 1 in 16, 1 in 64 and 1 in 256 for one, two, three and four traits respectively. From these simple examples it is abundantly clear that even with relatively low selection standards imposed and large numbers initially available for selection, the inclusion of several attributes very rapidly erodes numbers to a point at which very few individuals if any are satisfactory on all counts. At whatever point this occurs, finely balanced compromises—involving the trading off of strengths in some attributes against weaknesses in others—inevitably have to be made (Table 5).

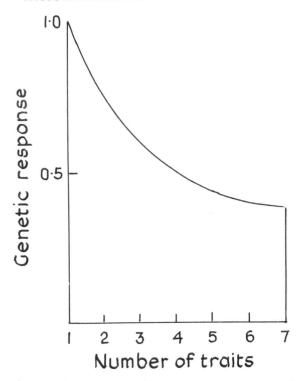

Fig. 11. The effect of introducing additional traits into a selection programme on the genetic response in milk yield (n.b. equal selection pressure applied to each trait).

Since loss of selection pressure in the primary traits caused by the introduction of other attributes is inevitable and can be very costly, their inclusion can only be justified in circumstances in which they can be shown, clearly and conclusively, to enhance the overall value of the *entire* response pattern. For precisely the same reasons that birds in hands are valued more highly than birds in bushes, hopeful expectations are not sufficient in themselves to justify the inclusion of an attribute in a selective breeding programme, however important or desirable it may appear to be. A failure to acknowledge this principle, culminating in the presence of inappropriate traits amongst the selection criteria, probably represents the commonest and most debilitating source of

Table 5. Compromises in selection—the effect of including a second trait (milking rate) in the selection programme on sire superiority in the primary trait (fat yield)

Sire groups	Average fat yield (kg)	Milking rate (kg/min)
Sire group 1	294.8	1.21
Sire group 2	275.3	2.22*
Sire group 3	274.8	2.04*
Sire group 4	269.4	1.63
Sire group 5	268.5	1.28
Sire group 6	262.4	1.66
Sire group 7	262.3	1.89
Sire group 8	261.2	1.50
Sire group 9	260.1	2.47*
Sire group 10	259.3	2.37*
Best 4—fat yield only	278.6	1.78
Best 4—milking rate only	267.6 (−11.0)	2.28 (+0.50)
Best 4—fat yield + rate	268.3 (−10.3)	2.16 (+0.38)

avoidable inefficiency in most current dairy cattle breeding programmes.

In practice, rather few attributes are genetically independent. Thus, some of the many genes that are known to influence milk yield also appear to affect body size, milk compositional quality, milking speed and many other characteristics of greater or lesser interest and commercial importance (Table 6). By induction of a series of correlated changes in other attributes, selection for one trait may elicit unexpected and still unrecognised changes in traits far removed from the characteristic for which selection was applied in the first place. For example, it is conceivable that selection for milk yield may influence the susceptibility of an animal to mastitis—not through any direct and immediate causal genetic link between the two but rather through a series of indirect genetic linkages via milking speed and teat shape and form. Once such remote causal relationships have been established, their treatment is usually straightforward. However, confronted by the presence of such possibilities, the recognition and determination of cause and effect

Table 6. Genetic correlations between first-lactation milk yield and other important components of productivity and behaviour

Lifetime yield	0.80–0.90
Weight of fat, protein, milk solids	0.70–0.90
Fat %, protein %, solids %	0.30–0.50
Milking speed	0.00
Temperament	0.00
Reproductive failure	0.00
Mastitis susceptibility	0.10
Type score	−0.20
Length of productive life	0.75

relationships has to remain a matter for specialised study and treatment.

However complicated and disconcerting the problems posed by genetic linkages of this kind may be, their implications and consequences for selective breeding practice must be understood by anyone wishing to fully exploit all opportunities. With respect to dairy herd improvement, the immediate consequences are twofold:

1. An indirect response, where desirable, may be sufficient in itself to entirely obviate a need to apply any direct selection. For example, an increase in body size elicited by selection for improved productivity may be sufficient to entirely remove the need to select for body size itself. Indirect responses of an undesirable nature may necessitate counter-selection or the introduction of monitoring systems as a protective device against the emergence of weaknesses such as stress-related conditions.

2. The presence of desirable and undesirable genetic correlations immediately influences the proportion of animals that exhibit genetic superiority or inferiority in several attributes. Where 1 in 4 animals may be expected to exceed average in two genetically independent traits, this expectation may rise as high as 1 in 3 or fall as low as 1 in 5—according to the strength and direction of the genetic linkage. These effects are observed in practice in the difficulties experienced in identifying animals that

exhibit a marked superiority in two directions—for example, in milk yield and milk compositional quality—where the presence of a negative genetic correlation severely reduces the numbers of animals that qualify on both counts.

In general, the indirect responses evoked by selection for productivity in dairy cattle appear to be favourable and to preclude a need for counter-selection or monitoring. Studies of high- and low-yielding cows in many localities have revealed unexpected indirect benefits in aspects of animal performance and behaviour that could not have been achieved by means of direct selection (Tables 7 and 8). Whilst it may seem reasonable to suppose that the highly productive animal must differ in many fundamental respects from her less productive herdmate, demonstrations of the fact that she tends to graze more selectively, to masticate and ruminate more efficiently, to respond more favourably to human and animal contact, to maintain peak yields longer and to manipulate body reserves more rapidly and effectively—all achieved in the absence of any direct conscious selection for any of these attributes—is highly reassuring. Despite an obvious need to maintain a close watch to prevent undesirable side effects of selection from emerging, it seems that many of the fears expressed from time to time concerning the risks associated with intense selection for increased productivity are not substantiated by the evidence available.

Table 7. Differences in production and food conversion efficiency between daughters of bulls of high and low breeding value

	Difference in production %	Difference in efficiency %
Milk yield (kg)	27	15
Fat-corrected milk (kg)	23	12
Total solids	19	9
Food intake	11	—

Source: Hind, E., Animal Breeding Research Organisation Report, 1979.

Table 8. The performance characteristics of cows with high and low genetic index ratings

Number of animals	29	27
Genetic index rating	127	101
Condition score at calving	4.8	4.7
Change in condition score during lactation	−0.7	0
Daily yield of fat in final 2 weeks of lactation	0.46	0.35
DM intake/kg fat	21.7	26.2
Yield of fat/hectare (kg)	569	483

Source: *Dairy Farming Annual* (1981), Massey University.

Chapter 5

HERD FOUNDATION

THE ESTABLISHMENT of an entirely new dairy herd is an unusual and noteworthy event at a time of contracting herd numbers throughout the Developed World. Nevertheless, the problems confronting the initiate are still the time-honoured ones that continue to generate passion and endless controversy wherever and whenever two or more farmers meet—namely, which breed type to adopt and from which source to procure the foundation material. With the majority severely constrained by lack of finance, only a fortunate few are able to begin a career in milk production with a herd that measures up to their ideal specification. Against the overriding and urgent need to generate the largest possible income at lowest cost, either numbers or quality or breed of preference are inevitably compromised.

The genetic status of a herd at its inception determines and pre-conditions its behaviour and achievements for many decades thereafter. Similarly, animal characteristics present in the foundation stock tend to remain prominent and relatively intractable features of the herd for long periods of time, changing only slowly in response to corrective measures applied by the owner. Thus a herd initially characterised by animals of fiery temperament or inadequate milking traits tends to continue to display these same undesirable attributes, if only in chronic or latent form, for several successive animal generations. For this reason alone, care and expertise invested in the selection of the foundation stock are likely to be amply repaid throughout the entire subsequent life-history of the herd to a much greater extent than similar efforts expended later. In the construction of any edifice that is intended to endure, economy and faulty workmanship in laying the foundations serves only to invite the chronic and persistent structural weaknesses that are sure to emerge at a later date.

The life-history of a typical dairy herd tends to follow a conventional and entirely predictable pattern—the classical diminishing-response curve characteristic of most small business enterprises. Whilst unusual local or temporal events—for example, the emergence of an exceptional stock bull or a change of ownership—may engender many exceptions to the general rule, in the normal case most of the improvement achieved throughout the lifetime of a dairy herd tends to be accomplished in the early years following its foundation—in many cases as an immediate consequence of eradicating the faults brought in by the foundation material.

Whether this evolutionary pattern merely reflects the ageing of the farmer himself or, possibly, a natural human reaction to early success or, even, an inability on the part of animals and management systems to continue to respond to increased pressure, is immaterial to the present question. Whatever the explanation may be, the dairy cattle population at any point in time contains a mixture of recently established herds displaying rapid responses to drastic treatments applied by their youthful, enthusiastic and impoverished owners, mature herds struggling to maintain their impetus and competitive status and aged herds displaying all the outward and inward signs of senility, decay and decline. For the latter to recover their former status once the pattern of decay has become established is almost as rare an event as that of a declining breed reattaining its former status.

Within dairy herds, the responses induced by the application of one set of priorities tend to bring about a reallocation of the priorities themselves. Thus any success achieved in one direction tends to reduce the need to continue to exert similar pressure in the same direction thereafter and to divert attention to other aspects of the business formerly considered to be of secondary importance. Having attended to the immediate problem of establishing a productive and profitable dairy unit—a process which usually involves initial neglect of other important attributes—most producers subsequently direct their efforts elsewhere, for instance towards the removal of factors that affect animal survival or

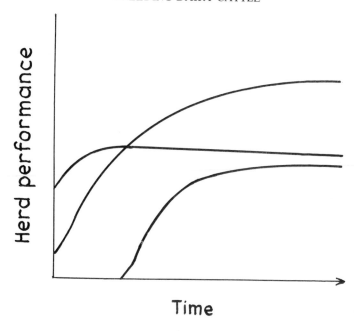

Fig. 12. Typical herd response curves illustrating the importance of the initial genetic status of the herd on its subsequent achievements.

the removal of animals which, for a variety of reasons, fail to conform to established standards and norms of behaviour. Consequently, the objectives and current priorities of each individual dairy farmer tend to differ from those of his neighbour according to his past achievements, present status and future ambitions—a fact of life too often ignored by those responsible for the provision of professional services and guidance to the industry.

The idealised herd profiles illustrated in Figure 12 have been chosen deliberately to depict the consequences of such dynamic changes occurring simultaneously within the population and also to demonstrate the importance of the initial launching point. Despite the rapid and substantial improvement achieved in one of the herds, its performance never overcomes the handicap imposed by defective foundation material and, consequently, never succeeds in matching or surpassing that of other herds with which it is competing. For the individual, the effect of commencing business at a high genetic level utilising the best material available to him at the time is to dispense with the many years of culling and expensive corrective treatment needed to compensate for entirely avoidable initial inadequacy, errors of judgement, compromise and inexperience.

CHOICE OF BREED

The historical processes by which cattle populations have become aggregated into distinctive breed types and varieties may have been necessary in order to introduce a semblance of order into what was previously chaos but, at the same time, have proved extremely costly in imposing a set of constraints and restrictive practices on cattle breeding that still complicate and diminish genetic possibilities.

With the introduction of formal herdbooks in the nineteenth century, embryonic breed types began to emerge in essentially the form in which we recognise them today. Charged initially with the task of recording parentage for purposes of reference and authentification, Breed Associations now fulfil many other functions. Their success in raising the concept and pursuit of breed purity to a level that is now preserved, protected and enshrined in legislation tends to conceal the recent mixed origins of most breeds, to diminish freedom of choice in the selection of mating partners, to encourage irrational marketing and pricing mechanisms and to discourage the formation of new breeds. The difficulties and anomalies associated with the concept of breed purity and its preservation are well exemplified in the case of the Friesian and Holstein types in Britain at the present day and also in the difficulties experienced by all breed societies in coming to terms with colour variants within the usual administrative framework.

While such distinctions between animal types may be of no biological significance, they do influence trading and introduce procedural obstacles and complications that have to be acknowledged, accommodated and resolved. For present purposes, breed titles are used merely as convenient descriptive labels and should not be taken to imply a distinct genetic identity or exclusiveness.

For anyone fortunate enough to inherit an established dairy herd the question of breed choice does not present itself with the same starkness and urgency as it does for those faced with the immediate problem of stocking and utilising empty fields and buildings. By the same token, the unique opportunity to introduce the most desirable animal type from the start avails itself only to the newcomer.

However, whether starting from nothing or merely contemplating the possibility of changing from one breed type to another, the choice in any particular instance may be influenced by a host of considerations not all of which can be directly attributed to breed merit or profit maximisation motives. Thus sentiment and tradition, aesthetics and fashion may play as large a part in reaching decisions as local peculiarities of supply and demand, climate, soil type and building layout and design. In many instances financial considerations compel owners to introduce a breed type or mixture of breed types not of their own choosing with a view to changing to the preferred type as soon as circumstances permit—a course of action not to be commended to anyone wishing to maximise his long-term prospects of stability and success.

Assuming breed choice to be an entirely open matter, dictated solely by the commercial merits of the many breed types potentially available, the ultimate choice has to favour the particular animal type considered most likely to achieve the long- and short-term objectives of the business in fullest measure—a specification that does not exclude crossbred animals from the reckoning.

At the present time, the most desirable animal for most producers is one that is capable of sustaining long periods of continuous and heavy production of milk solids whilst also supplying at annual intervals calves that can command a useful price for rearing and fattening purposes—a demanding specification that clearly envisages and encompasses a long, healthy and fertile sojourn in the dairy herd and stresses the commercial importance of the cow/calf unit.

Table 9. Differences between Friesian and Jersey cattle in productivity and food conversion efficiency

	% difference in production (F/J)	% difference in food conversion (kg milk/kg food)
Milk yield	+53	+28
Fat-corrected milk	+30	+ 9
Total solids	+25	+ 4
Food intake	+22	—

Source: Hind, E., Animal Breeding Research Organisation Report, 1979.

Following a series of comprehensive and sophisticated breed comparisons in recent years it is now generally agreed that most of the useful genetic variation in productive efficiency between dairy cows is to be found between individuals within a breed rather than between the breeds themselves (Table 9). For practical purposes this conclusion tends to confirm the traditional argument that a good cow is a good cow whichever breed type she may happen to conform to. Provided, therefore, that the comparison is confined strictly to the efficiency and profitability with which milk is produced, the question of breed type would seem to be of peripheral importance.

However, with additional sources of revenue potentially available in the cull-cow and the surplus calf, breeds possessing a capacity to grow quickly to a large mature size and produce an acceptable carcase at the end of the process are at a distinct advantage. The possession of these attributes, combined with the very real benefits obtained from numerical strength, are sufficient in themselves to explain and fully justify current preferences for Holstein cattle throughout Western Europe and the entire Developed World.

The importance of body size as a criterion of selection in its own right has been disputed for many years. That larger animals tend to be more productive and profitable than their smaller herdmates is a well-established and commonly observed phenomenon. Furthermore, the underlying genetic relationships between production and body size are such that, even in the absence of any deliberate selection for increased size, larger animals will tend to be favoured by selection for productivity.

Nevertheless, the advantages conferred by a large frame are not absolute and examples of small animals that match or excel their larger herdmates in productivity are not difficult to find. Consequently any direct selection for increased body size which places productive small cows at a disadvantage can only be exercised at the expense of efficient selection. If the primary objective of the selection process is to maximise productive efficiency, there can be no place in the list of selection priorities for body size per se.

Though the purebred animal tends to dominate the dairy cattle scene, the tradition bears further examination in view of the many virtues known to reside in offspring of mixed parentage. For the individual faced with the immediate problem of establishing a herd, the attractions of crossbred animals are immediate and obvious, namely their reduced purchase price and tolerance of sub-optimal conditions and treatment. Whilst uniform, vigorous and often highly productive in hybrid form, the propagation of crossbred cattle presents difficulties in identifying and maintaining superior parental stocks and in finding profitable and secure outlets for products.

An irrational but widespread and profound distaste for mongrelisation in any shape or form has created a situation in which any crossbred animals that are maintained on farms tend to be the inevitable by-product of a change from one breed type to another as opposed to the product of a long-term crossbreeding strategy.

In recent times, the attractions of crossbreeding have been overtaken and diminished by the emergence of a purebred, the Friesian–Holstein, which appears to excel the best of its crosses with all other breeds.

SOURCES OF MATERIAL

However obvious and important the need to commence business with animals of superior genetic merit may be, the means by which to accomplish this at realistic cost are much less apparent.

The purchase of foundation and replacement stock calls for special expertise, initiative and good fortune. The purchaser of livestock enjoys access to few of the devices that serve to protect consumers of most other products against fraud, deception and their own incredulity. The vendor, on the other hand, is constrained by few codes of professional practice and, in many cases, is known to exploit the situation to dispose of defective material. Given the many factors that can contribute to a failure on the part of an animal to match expectations and the long time interval elapsing between purchase and the testing of performance attributes, responsibility for failure is impossible to attribute unequivocally and normal redress procedures unworkable.

The traditional sources and orthodox procedures by which stock exchange hands confront the newcomer with an impossible choice—that of incurring exorbitant costs by attempting to buy in competition with many others in places where the risks of failure or of importing disease are minimal, or else of buying animals of unknown history from unknown suppliers who offer no sureties. The problem is one that clearly calls for the exercise of imagination and for the adoption of unconventional methods.

Fortunately, opportunities of an unorthodox and unsuspected nature do exist and can be exploited on occasion by those possessed of the enterprise and energy needed to seek them out. Such procedures tend to be highly opportunistic—available only for short periods of time to those first to recognise them and to be rapidly extinguished as soon as their availability becomes a matter of common knowledge. A few examples will suffice to illustrate the point.

All established dairy herds continually shed surplus animals either as cull cows or as surplus calves. Amongst the former are included animals possessed of desirable qualities culled reluctantly by their owners for involuntary or mistaken reasons—the infertile cow that subsequently breeds, the animal calving at an inconvenient time of year and the productive, fertile but slightly unsightly animal bearing the relics of disease (see Table 10). Amongst the younger

Table 10. Conception and embryo survival rate amongst dairy cows culled for failure to conceive to one or more inseminations

| | Days after insemination | | | |
	3–6	16–19	40–49	
Number of cows inseminated	25	25	23	73
Number of cows conceiving	21	14	16	51
Number of viable embryos	13	12	13	38
Embryo survival rate (%)	100	67	76	79
Percentage of cows with normal embryos	52	48	57	52

Source: O'Farrell, K. J. *et al.*, *Veterinary Record* **112**:95 (1983).

animals, the unwanted red calf or the heifer that fails to conform to the desired behaviour pattern can usually be procured for little more than disposal value.

Whilst not necessarily attractive in appearance, the performance, health status and breeding merit of such outcasts is not adversely affected by the condition that brought about their disposal. Their potential as foundation material is infinitely greater than that of animals of more orthodox appearance purchased from an unknown background in the local market.

For those willing to sacrifice convention and conformity for a short period of time, many opportunities are available by which to establish a dairy herd of excellent genetic status at nominal cost.

Chapter 6

FEMALE SELECTION

THE FACT that the functions of the two sexes and their relative importance in the breeding of the dairy herd are still disputed by breeders and animal scientists reflects a failure on the part of the former to acknowledge the supreme importance of differences in fecundity between the two sexes and of the latter to admit the importance to producers of many animal attributes that cannot be accommodated within a conventional progeny testing scheme.

Whilst an abiding obsession with cow families and female lines of descent on the part of stockmen exposed daily to the virtues and shortcomings of milking cows may be understandable, it has long been established in repeated studies of the two sexes that, when tested bulls are used, the variation observed in the performance of females in the dairy herd can be more fully and satisfactorily explained by reference to their male ancestors and relatives than by reference to dams, granddams, cousins, sisters and aunts. The specimen production pedigrees shown in Figures 13 and 14 illustrate the point.

To the extent that milk production is a sex-limited trait expressed only in the female, her importance in the mating and breeding process would seem to be paramount. The further observation that both parents contribute equally to the genetic constitution of their offspring would also appear to confirm the importance of the maternal contribution.

Before the introduction of commercial AI services both arguments were fully valid and the males were quite properly assigned a subsidiary, supportive role in herd development programmes. At the time, males used as stock bulls on farms were a dangerous commodity of unknown or dubious genetic merit, assessable only on outward appearance, temperament

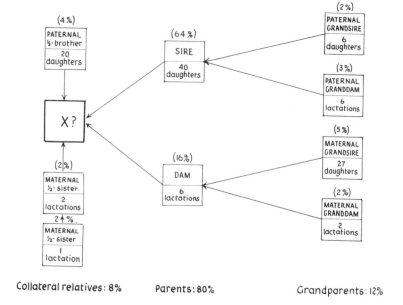

Collateral relatives: 8%   Parents: 80%   Grandparents: 12%

Fig. 13. A specimen production pedigree illustrating the relative contribution of different sources of information to the estimated breeding value of an individual animal (X).

and tenuous expectations derived from the performance of ancestors and remote relatives, while the individual qualities of each female in the herd were at least as familiar to their owners as they are today.

The introduction of commercial AI services not only removed the stock bull from farms but also, through the progeny test process with which AI rapidly became linked, raised the importance and potential genetic contribution of the male sex to levels that far exceeded that of any individual female (see Figure 5). At the same time, the primary responsibility for male selection was removed from the farming community and, for better or worse, transferred to specialists and administrators far removed from the farmyard and milking shed.

These very fundamental changes in the status of the two

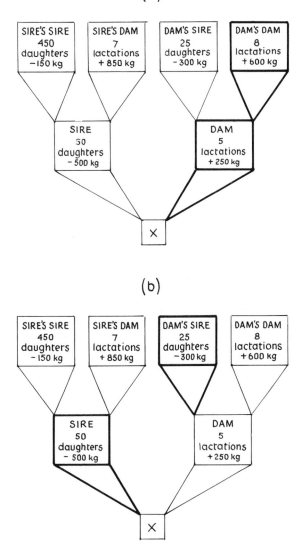

Fig. 14. Alternative views of a production
pedigree—interpreted in terms of (a) female lines of descent
and (b) paternal relationships.

Table 11. The accuracy of a cow's own performance records expressed in terms of the equivalent number of effective daughters (W) and the repeatability (r) of a progeny test proof

Number of records	Equivalent number of effective daughters (W)	Repeatability (r)
1	5.0	0.50
2	7.3	0.57
3	9.0	0.61
5	11.0	0.65
10	13.0	0.68

sexes, initiated by a breakthrough in reproductive technology, not only permitted the males to propagate very many more female offspring than any female (and thereby spread their genetic influence further afield) but also allowed the genetic merit of the bulls to be evaluated directly across many daughters in many different herd environments. Consequently, any male found to transmit desirable qualities to the next generation is now able to pass them on to many thousands of first- and later-generation descendants.

The breeding merits of a female, on the other hand, can still only be assessed largely on the strength of her own performance in a single herd and, once evaluated, transmitted only to the very few daughters she is able to bear in the course of her brief lifetime. Notoriously sensitive as her performance records are known to be to a host of special treatment and chance effects which conceal and distort the appraisal of her genetic merit, the suspicion and caution quite properly exercised in the case of a bull with daughters in a single herd must be applied in even greater measure to the female, however well documented she may happen to be.

Thus the degree of confidence with which a bull may be used in any particular mating normally exceeds that of his partner to a considerable degree. This particular discrepancy between the two sexes is illustrated in Table 11 in which the accuracy of female selection is expressed in terms of the numbers of daughters contributing to a progeny test. It is clear that even the oldest animals in the herd can rarely achieve a status comparable with that of a bull tested across ten to fifteen daughters (see Figure 9).

The very large number of proven bulls potentially available at all times through AI offers the farmer a choice that may be exercised entirely at his own discretion, at times and for reasons of his own choosing. This very substantial degree of freedom and flexibility in male selection contrasts markedly with a fixed female resource in which freedom to exercise choice and express selection preferences is severely circumscribed by the perpetual need to retain a high proportion of the females anyway, regardless of their qualities and condition, and by the desire to employ the female culling and replacement process for a number of purposes other than the pursuit of genetic improvement.

For all of these reasons, herd development strategies based on or conditioned by traditional concepts of female families and female lines of descent fail to exploit selection opportunities to the full and only serve to invite the contradictions, disappointments and anomalous results that invariably characterise programmes containing misplaced priorities. Their replacement by alternative procedures in which the dominant role of the male sex is fully acknowledged and exploited and in which female selection is applied merely to minimise or erase the problems introduced by the bulls is an essential prerequisite for sustained genetic progress in the herd.

For planning and descriptive purposes, the female culling and replacement process may be viewed in cross-section as an annual input–output exercise, a herd cleansing process whereby a relatively uniform group of young recruits is introduced at the expense of an older group no longer required (Figure 15). Alternatively, culling and herd replacement may be viewed as a protracted, repetitive exercise extending over many years whereby an initial group of recruits is regularly subjected to inspection and examination by their owner and progressively eroded and modified by preferential selection and ageing as their career advances (Figure 16). Both descriptive processes are useful and illuminating in seeking to understand the mechanics and

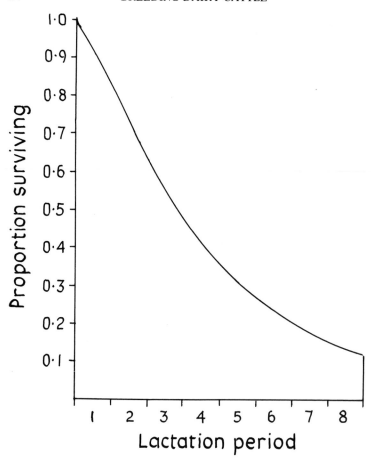

Fig. 15. Herd survival—the proportion of animals surviving to different ages.

consequences of the culling process and the opportunities it offers for long-term herd improvement.

In stable well-established herds 25–33 per cent of the milking section of the herd is normally replaced annually, a process which imposes an average productive lifespan of three to four lactations and permits complete replacement of the entire herd at three to four-year intervals if so desired. Though the proportion replaced may vary considerably from

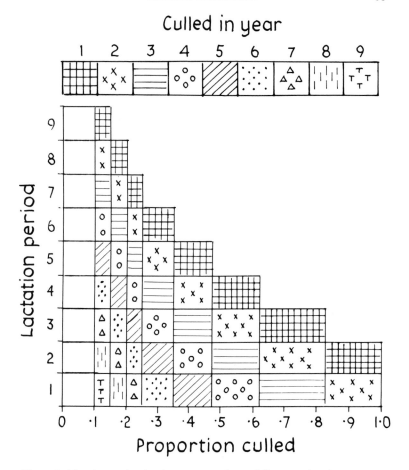

*Fig. 16. Herd survival—the proportion of first and subsequent
calvers culled in successive years.*

time to time and herd to herd in response to market
opportunities or a wish to increase or decrease the size of the
herd, the total amount of culling applied in a herd and its
distribution across lactation periods tend to reflect the
management policy and priorities of the owner, supplying
information that may be used diagnostically to identify
weaknesses in the process and neglected opportunities for
improved selection (Figure 17).

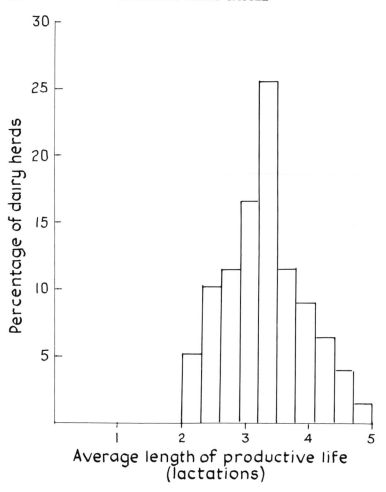

Fig. 17. Variation between herds in average length of productive life.

Source: Young, G. B., *et al.*, *Vet. Rec.* **113**:107 (1983).

In contrast to the male selection process, which in most instances is employed specifically and exclusively to promote genetic improvement in the herd, the opportunity to cull and replace females is utilised by farmers for a number of different purposes. In many herds, the wish to maintain tight seasonal patterns of calving can result in the retention and

Table 12. Milk yield characteristics of registered and non-registered Holstein cows in the United States

	Registered	Non-registered	Difference
Number of animals	143,396	154,483	
Average milk yield (kg)	+114	+254	140
Average sire value (kg)	+ 66	+207	207

Source: Powell, R. L., *The Advanced Animal Breeder* **XXX**:9 (1982).

disposal of animals for reasons entirely unconnected with their intrinsic genetic merit, a policy which in extreme cases can lead to the replacement of genetically superior females by inferior stock (see Table 12). In other herds, the disposal of animals for purely opportunistic reasons may dominate the culling process to such an extent as to entirely preclude all opportunities to exercise selection preferences—a practice which, when adopted in herds that regularly supply breeding stock to others, can lead to an anachronistic situation whereby animals migrate from genetically inferior herds into herds of superior genetic status (Table 12).

Though the effects and implications may not be so immediately obvious, perhaps, the common practice whereby younger animals are mated to bulls of another breed in order to secure a better price for calves or easier calving has precisely the same effect in further eroding selection opportunities within the herd. Whilst perfectly legitimate as an exercise in herd management and possibly highly profitable in terms of short-term advantage, any manipulation of the female breeding resource in these ways for purposes of convenience or immediate gain can only be admitted and accomplished at the ultimate expense of long-term possibilities for herd development.

Insofar as the culling mechanism is actively and deliberately exploited for herd cleansing, healing and corrective purposes, it appears to be utilised in the first instance to control and modify animal health and fertility, behaviour and constitution—that is, as the ultimate sanction

Table 13. The major sources of culling and wastage in dairy herds

| | Lactation numbers | | |
	1–3	4–6	7–9
Reproductive failure	0.37	0.33	0.26
Low production	0.24	0.16	0.10
Mastitis	0.09	0.17	0.14
Udder faults	0.06	0.10	0.09
Defective legs and feet	0.01	0.04	0.05
Calving problems	0.03	0.02	0.02

Source: Young, G. B., *et al.*, *Vet. Rec.* **113**:107 (1983).

by which the most obvious and deficient failures of other treatments are pinpointed and rejected (Table 13).

To the extent that disease, infertility and accidental loss enforce the disposal of desirable as well as undesirable members of the milking herd, the culling and replacement of females is not conducted at the entire discretion of the owner. However necessary and effective the disposal process may be in eradicating the immediate problems and hazards posed by the presence of disease, infertility and physical infirmity, it is important to appreciate that *any* wastage of this kind—whether enforced or not—constitutes selection for attributes that exhibit little or no genetic variation. However stringent and scrupulous herd owners may be in disposing of diseased, injured and infertile stock, neither the animals that escape the process nor their descendants in the next generation derive any genetic benefit from the practice.

Having utilised the culling mechanisms for the necessary and important purpose of maintaining a healthy and fertile herd, the residual scope remaining to apply preferential selection for attributes that are capable of responding to selective breeding is very small indeed (Table 13).

In this situation, any measure that serves to reduce wastage in the milking herd or amongst the replacement stock is likely to confer immediate benefits in releasing additional animal resources amongst which more effective genetic selection may then be applied.

Studies of the culling process have revealed the extent to which selection priorities in dairy herds vary and change as the animal ages. In most commercial units, culling early in life appears to be mainly voluntary in nature and to be directed principally towards the primary production traits. Having attended to the immediate problems presented by young cows which fail to milk up to expectation or which fail to emerge from their first experience of calving in good shape, much of the culling applied thereafter appears to be directed or impelled towards the maintenance of fertility, health and constitutional soundness, with treatment preferences consistently expressed in favour of the more productive members of the herd. Animals exhibiting chronic disease, sub-optimal fertility or undesirable physical and behavioural attributes tend to be retained if highly productive and disposed of otherwise.

The cumulative effect of such practices, preferences and prejudices is a survival pattern in which the most important single identifiable determinant of longevity and lifetime performance is first-lactation production (Figures 18 and 19). The argument that selection for high productivity early in life is necessarily detrimental to longevity and lifetime performance or else somehow prejudicial to health and fertility is not supported by the evidence obtained from herd studies, tends to be contradicted by the observation that longevity does not appear to have diminished over the years in response to substantial increases in productivity and appears to derive plausibility only from a small number of exceptions to normal behavioural patterns.

Reassuring as this general conclusion may be, several anomalies and sources of inefficiency in female culling and selection processes have been identified and are amenable to immediate correction. Foremost amongst these may be cited:

- the tendency of many farmers to allow favoured animals a second chance to redeem an unsatisfactory first-lactation performance. Since very few of the animals to which the privilege is extended improve sufficiently thereafter to justify their continued retention (Figure 20), this particular practice tends to be both costly and ineffective.
- the tendency on the part of most farmers to cull or retain animals merely on the strength of their most recent

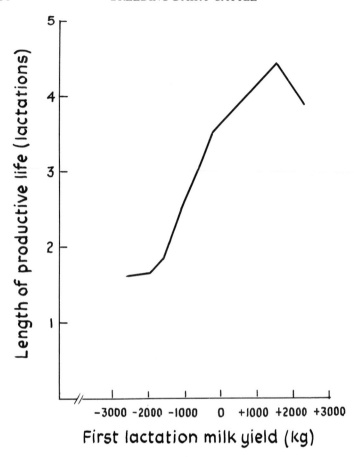

Fig. 18. The relationship between first lactation milk yield and length of productive life.

performance record, without reference either to earlier performance or to that of comparable animals in the herd. Exaggerated responses of this kind to what frequently turns out to be a temporary aberration on the part of the animal can result in inconsistent selection standards being applied and in the disposal of genetically superior stock.
• Diagnostic errors of the kind that cause healthy fertile

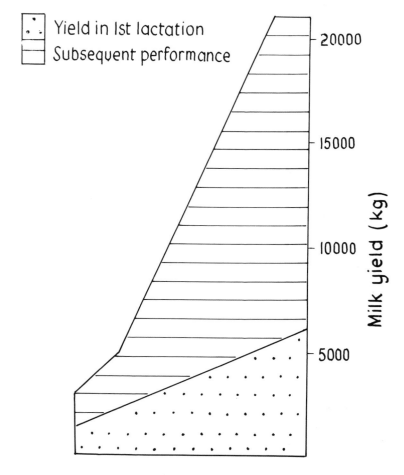

Fig. 19. The relationship between first lactation performance
and total lifetime yield.

animals to be disposed of in the mistaken belief that they
are barren or diseased (see Table 10).
● Cosmetic selection leading to the disposal of animals of
  inferior type status or of animals damaged by disease
  which, though possibly unsightly, are still productive and
  highly desirable as breeding stock.

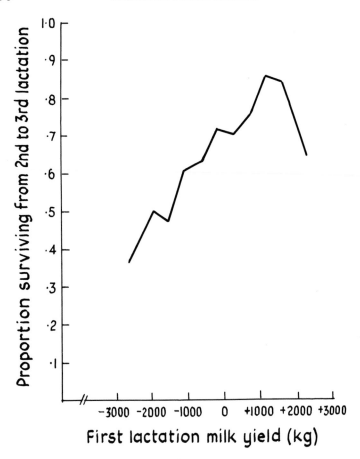

Fig. 20. The relationship between first lactation milk yield and the proportion surviving to commence a third lactation.

Confronted by a need to include many attributes, to draw comparisons between animals of different ages and to make appropriate allowances for the merits and faults of ancestors and close relatives, it is natural to look first to conventional index selection methods to supply a general solution to the problem of ranking animals in order of merit.

Unfortunately, whilst high index ratings may provide a useful objective to aim for (see Chapter 8), generalised index procedures have rarely proved sufficiently versatile to meet the varied and constantly changing needs and priorities of the individual herd. Unique index selection methods, for use within a single herd, tend to be too complex and unrewarding to justify their introduction.

Since the animals that contribute most effectively to herd improvement tend to be located at either extreme of the distribution (i.e. the highly productive cows to be retained at all costs and the unproductive specimens to be disposed of at the first opportunity), they are readily distinguishable by methods much less complicated and sophisticated.

In conclusion, it is clear that the female sex affords only limited scope for actively promoting improvement by selective breeding but extends an excellent facility by which to remove defective material from the herd, to manipulate calving patterns and to attend to attributes of secondary importance that cannot be accommodated within the sire selection programme. This being the case, a herd development strategy which directs and concentrates effort and expertise in the places most likely to respond to it and withdraws it from those sectors that do not respond, is likely to prove both effective and economical.

Chapter 7

MALE SELECTION

FORMULATED BEFORE the introduction of artificial insemination, the simplistic statement to the effect that the bull
constitutes half the dairy herd may once have contained a
germ of truth. In today's very different conditions, however, it
greatly understates the potential of the male sex and can be
held to apply only in herds not yet utilising the AI service to
full advantage.

In terms of its contribution to dairy herd improvement, the
superior AI-proven bull, used repeatedly in successive
generations in matings with daughters and granddaughters of
superior proven bulls, now provides almost all of the impetus
by which genetic change is, or can be, accomplished.

This latent potential, still frequently unrecognised and
even today rarely fully and effectively exploited, constitutes a
virtually untapped source of genetic improvement for the
future. No amount of female selection within dairy herds,
however intensely and assiduously applied, can exert a similar
influence or adequately compensate for deficiencies and
neglect in the processes by which bulls are chosen and used.

The identification of bulls suitable for use in the dairy herd
and the deployment of their semen thereafter regularly
confronts every dairy farmer with decision-making processes
that are crucial in determining the characteristics of his herd
and the future well-being of his business enterprise.

With a very extensive range of breeding material available
through AI and with new bulls and new information emerging
all the time, the achievement of an effective sire selection
programme requires that the progeny record of every
available AI-proven bull is carefully scrutinised—preferably
on each occasion that a choice is exercised but, failing that, at
least on the first appearance of a newcomer within the proven

bull stud. Whilst many bulls may be discarded immediately for one obvious reason or another, the final selection inevitably comes to rest between several candidates that each display a variety of strengths and weaknesses of greater or less degree and importance.

The typical record of a progeny tested bull contains a bewildering array of factual and circumstantial evidence relating not only to daughter productivity and type, temperament and behaviour, milking and calving characteristics and so on, but also to the precision and reliability of the test proof itself, the price and availability of semen and, in some instances, the conception rates of the bulls and the size and suitability of the offspring for beef production.

Since few users of AI services are able to expend the time and effort needed to inspect progeny groups on their own behalf and to seek out the opinions and experiences of owners of progeny, the assessment of sire merit has usually to be achieved on the strength of the printed record alone. In these circumstances, the assessment calls for the application of an unusual degree of skill and expertise in interpreting test records, in combining a great deal of information of various kinds according to the priorities of the individual concerned and, finally, in discounting the extravagant claims and propaganda that usually accompany the test report. Having accomplished all this, the problems involved in determining the number of bulls to be used in the herd at any one time and of deciding how extensively to utilise each bull and for how long still remain unanswered.

Faced with such daunting, complex and time-consuming processes, it is not surprising that many have chosen to adopt quick and easy solutions by using whatever semen happens to be available at the time a cow is inseminated or, alternatively, of making their herds available as test-beds for AI organisations to use, thereby avoiding the intricacies of the selection processes altogether and allowing the failures as well as the successes of the AI development programme access to their herds.

Whilst either course of action meets the primary need to get cows with-calf and may be commendable on grounds of simplicity alone, those who choose to exercise them have not

Table 14. Differences in the merit of AI and natural service bulls used in milk recorded herds

	Milk yield (kg)	Fat yield (kg)	Protein yield (kg)
AI sires	+219	+8.8	+6.0
Natural service sires	+ 97	+4.6	+3.0
Difference	122	4.2	3.0

Source: Milk Marketing Board: Report of the Breeding and Production Organisation, 1982.

only permitted ultimate control of an important element of their business to be transferred to others with a lesser interest in its success, but have also foregone a major opportunity for herd development that cannot be made good by other means. In today's competitive climate, herds failing to utilise AI at all are likely to figure prominently amongst those ceasing milk production (Table 14).

For those prepared to make the effort, to set their sights high enough and to recognise and exploit only what is possible—as opposed to what may be desirable—a steady and sustained response can be guaranteed (Table 15). Whilst sire selection and usage may be a complex and inexact science

Table 15. The effect of variation in the intensity of sire selection on sire superiority in milk production

Proportion selected	Milk yield (kg)	Fat yield (kg)	Protein yield (kg)	Fat %	Protein %
0.01	+490	+20	+14	+0.24	+0.10
0.05	+326	+13	+ 9	+0.15	+0.06
0.10	+252	+11	+ 7	+0.12	+0.04
0.20	+171	+ 7	+ 4	+0.07	+0.02

Source: Milk Marketing Board, Report of the Breeding and Production Organisation, 1982.

Table 16. Progeny tests of sires and sons

	Average sire value (kg milk)	Number of sons tested	Number of +rated sons	% of +rated sons	Average value of sons (kg milk)
11 High sires	+610	5,588	4,719	84	+200
11 Average sires	+275	2,101	1,134	54	+ 3
11 Low sires	−131	1,844	288	12	−190
	+251	9,533	6,081	64	+ 86

generating disappointments and exceptions to rules, it nevertheless remains a science in which the disciplined observation and application of a number of well-proven principles and techniques will, in time, offer benefits surpassing anything to be derived from speculative breeding of the kind still favoured in many of the more prominent and fashionable pedigree herds. The very high degree of certitude with which the attributes of immediate commercial value respond to selection is illustrated in Table 16.

FACTORS AFFECTING SIRE SELECTION AND USAGE

The AI-proven bulls routinely used in dairy herds have already undergone a varied and protracted series of screening and selection processes before dairy farmers are allowed an opportunity to exercise their own preferences and impose their own selection priorities through their semen purchases.

Up to an age of 6–7 years almost all of the selection applied within the male sex is determined by agencies operating outside the herd. For example, the initial mating decision that predetermines the parentage of a young bull is usually specified in advance by a central testing organisation, as are the subsequent screening and selection processes normally applied shortly after birth, at point of entry to AI and on completion of the progeny test.

Consequently, the proven bulls amongst which farmers make their final choice of herd sires represent a small number of survivors of a process that has already detected and either documented or eliminated most of the gross abnormalities and deficiencies in respect of male fertility and daughter production, behaviour and type.

The selection decisions subsequently applied by the farmer in nominating bulls for use in the herd must not only acknowledge and accommodate the previous selection history of the bulls in question but must also seek to avoid the mistake of dissipating selection pressure on attributes that have already been adequately catered for.

The mechanics of the progeny testing process are such that any bull siring daughters that fail in any important respect to measure up to the diverse and exacting standards set by their owners are not likely to be retained for long within the proven bull stud. Thus, even in the absence of any direct overt selection amongst the bulls for improved daughter fertility, constitution, health status, milking characteristics and so on, any serious deficiency in any of these secondary traits is likely to have the immediate effect of reducing daughter yields and thereby diminishing the bull's immediate survival prospects. Consequently, for quite different reasons, bulls that survive the progeny testing process have already demonstrated a capacity to sire progeny of acceptable merit in all these respects and do not *have* to be further discriminated against on any of these particular counts.

RISK AVOIDANCE

The observation that the male sex, on completion of the testing phase, extends large possibilities for herd improvement has to be tempered by the knowledge that the injudicious use of bulls can also destroy or severely damage a herd over a relatively short period of time.

As in any other commercial enterprise, the prospects of success and failure in sire selection tend to be directly proportional to the magnitude and kind of risk that the individual is prepared to accommodate. For example, breeders dependent for their livelihood on stock sales and seeking to achieve a spectacular success in the showring or the means by which to propagate animals of a unique and original specification to offer prospective customers are compelled by circumstances to adopt different priorities, to accept high risks of failure and to practise speculative breeding measures of a kind that most others would not normally contemplate (e.g. close inbreeding, the use of inferior sires). That their products continue to find a ready sale despite widespread recognition of these anomalies remains one of the abiding mysteries of the cattle breeding scene. In the more typical situation, in which income is derived mainly from milk sales, the need to incur risks of such an abnormal, speculative and entirely avoidable nature does not arise.

The risks usually encountered in the selection and use of bulls in dairy herds are of two distinct and identifiable kinds—those arising from sampling and those attributable to ignorance and lack of understanding of the factors contributing to variation in animal and herd performance, both of which can cause bulls which may appear of equal merit to differ in their contribution to the herds in which they are used.

Even very large populations and groups of animals are subject to chance sampling effects of the kind that manifest themselves as grossly abnormal sex ratios at birth or—more appropriate still in the present context—as an unusual concentration of atypical daughters of a bull in a particular location. The pluses and minuses induced by sampling, which tend to cancel out when distributed across large populations, are often highly exaggerated and highly visible when concentrated in production units containing mere hundreds of animals. When experienced at herd level, the consequences can be crippling. The knowledge that the grosser deviations from normality caused by chance effects alone tend to be highly localised, infrequent and of short duration may be a source of considerable comfort to the majority but is of no assistance whatever to the individual unfortunate enough to experience them.

Some partial protection against the more damaging effects of sampling can be obtained by the adoption of breeding measures that enlarge the numerical size of the operational unit. In the context of sire usage in the dairy herd, this entails a reduction in the numbers of bulls used in order to generate progeny groups large enough to preclude or minimise the undesirable consequences of the atypical result. If sampling were the only consideration involved, then it follows that the use of a single proven bull throughout the entire herd would be an entirely appropriate protective measure to adopt as part of a risk avoidance strategy.

However, risks of another, entirely different, kind arise out of lack of knowledge and personal experience on the part of AI users of the many qualities of the bulls they are considering for use in their herds and also from a more widespread lack of understanding of many of the underlying factors contributing to variation between animals, herds and localities. Though some protection against ignorance and uncertainty can be secured by restricting the choice exclusively to bulls with reputable and reliable AI test proofs, this measure still fails to make full provision for the many important attributes of dairy animals that are not adequately accommodated within standard progeny testing procedures nor for interactions of the kind that cause the progeny of some bulls to react atypically to particular localised conditions (Figure 21). Interactions of this kind are known to exist but have not been explained, cannot be anticipated and diminish the confidence with which any single bull may be used. The problem is not restricted only to the sires standing at AI but applies in equal or greater measure to natural service situations.

Accordingly, protection against the major identifiable hazards in sire selection and usage calls for entirely contradictory courses of action at herd level. Though highly developed techniques for dealing with this seemingly intractable problem of quantifying risks and arriving at optimal solutions are available for other purposes (e.g. in actuarial work), they have not yet been extended into this particular area of activity.

In the absence of expert guidance in the formulation of optimal risk avoidance strategies, most users of AI services have been obliged to seek empirical solutions which may or may not be appropriate, causing some to use more bulls than they wish and others fewer than they may need. Faced with the same uncertainties, others have chosen to adopt

Sire value in :
- • low performance herds
- x average   ”   ”
- △ high   ”   ”

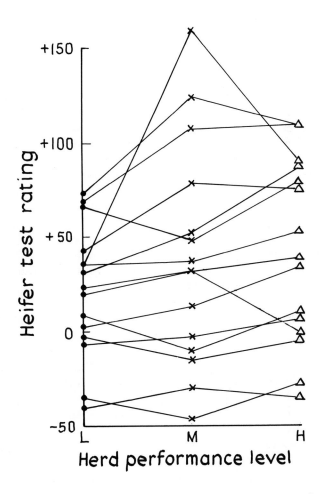

Fig. 21. Variation in the ranking of progeny groups in high,
average and low-performance herds.

additional screening processes of their own, repeating the progeny test in small samples of daughters in their own herds before proceeding to use a bull more extensively throughout the entire herd. On the strength of the purely pragmatic argument that the use of a single bull entails an unnecessarily high risk of failure and the use of many bulls the unnecessary sacrifice of selection pressure, the common practice of using 2–3 bulls simultaneously throughout the herd would appear to make adequate provision for the known risks involved.

The Promotion of Daughter Merit

Though risk awareness and avoidance may condition and constrain the sire selection process, the primary objective of most farmers in introducing bulls into the herd is to maximise the total merit of the next generation of females, either by the correction or removal of weaknesses present in their current stock or by the reinforcement of desirable characteristics already present.

Easy as it may be to identify and demonstrate total merit retrospectively in males and females that are considered to possess or display it, and easy as the concept may be to envisage in the mind's eye, the entity itself represents an entirely impractical planning objective, a complex interacting combination of genetic, special treatment and chance effects yielding an idealised specification in which strengths in one component are permitted to compensate for weaknesses elsewhere and which varies from place to place, time to time and person to person.

Despite recent advances in sire appraisal methods, the user of AI services seeking to determine the potential value of a bull for his own special circumstances is still reduced to seeking clues amongst the objective and subjective information contained in a typical sire proof. The common observation and experience of two bulls of apparently identical breeding merit which subsequently differ markedly in the contribution they make to the herds in which they are used illustrates the nature of the problem and demonstrates the failure of conventional progeny testing methods to supply all the relevant information needed to discriminate between bulls. Though many of the underlying causes that contribute to this unsatisfactory situation constitute occupational hazards of a kind that cannot be removed by additional testing and documentation, others are directly attributable to the extensive testing methods adopted and are therefore amenable to correction.

1. Daughter productivity

Whilst retaining total merit as the ultimate ideal, it is necessary for the reasons stated above to disentangle the important components of merit in order to arrive at practical selection criteria and methods most likely to secure it. Of the many attributes contributing to total merit, the ability of animals to sustain high levels of continuous production throughout their working career in the dairy herd is by far the most important.

Amongst the information contained in a test proof, the most direct and useful evidence of a bull's capacity to contribute daughters that meet this demanding and comprehensive specification is the herdmate or contemporary comparison estimate. Whatever particular form this value may assume in different progeny testing schemes around the globe and whatever modifications may be introduced to suit

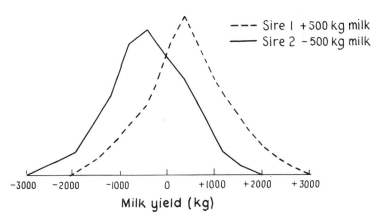

Fig. 22. *Variation in performance between daughters of bulls of high and low breeding merit.*

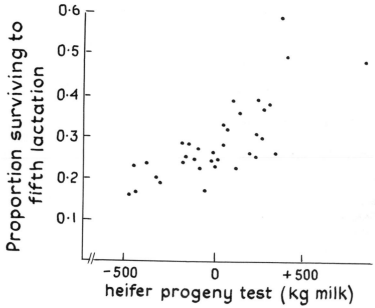

Fig. 23. The relationship between the progeny text rating of bulls and the survival of their daughters in dairy herds.

Source: Robertson, Alan and Barker, J. S. F., *Anim. Prod.* **8**:241 (1966).

local circumstances, in all cases the contemporary comparison estimate constitutes both a summary of daughter performance in the herds in which the bull has been used and also an index that may be used predictively to anticipate daughter performance in herds in which the bull may be used in future.

As a measure of the average performance of a typical daughter of a bull, the estimate provides a useful means by which to compare the potential breeding merit of different bulls but, in common with all other summation or averaging procedures, fails to reveal and explain the extent to which daughter and progeny group performance varies from herd to herd. Consequently, for those not familiar with the complex estimation procedures employed, the immediate relevance of the estimate and the probable outcome in their own herds of using bulls characterised by different contemporary comparison values are not immediately obvious. Similarly, when used as an index of lifetime performance and total merit, the value and reliability of a sire assessment derived essentially from the first lactation performance of a relatively small sample of daughters is not abundantly clear.

The difficulties now experienced by users of such information are no longer those of coming to terms with an unfamiliar concept but rather of determining to their own satisfaction how complete and dependable such estimates are as a guide to total merit and what additional need remains to utilise supplementary information relating to other characteristics.

The strong positive relationships between first lactation performance on the one hand and lifetime productivity, survival and longevity on the other, observed earlier amongst individual cows, are equally apparent amongst sire progeny groups (Figure 23). In general, the productive young cows propagated by bulls with high positive test ratings continue to exhibit a superior productivity later in life, outyielding and outliving the daughters of less highly rated sires. This superiority, which tends to be expressed across a wide range of management conditions and systems, is most clearly observed in high-yielding herds where variation in performance is least severely constrained by management practices.

Changes in the performance of sire progeny groups as they age are directly influenced by preferential culling. Intense culling amongst the daughters of the less highly rated bulls can conceal a bull's inability to sire productive older cows and contribute to widespread misconceptions regarding the relevance and suitability of sire proofs derived from first lactation records. Once the distortions introduced by the purely mechanical effects of preferential treatment and differential culling have been removed, the number of bulls siring daughters that fail to perform later in life according to the normal ageing patterns described above appears to be very small.

2. Selection for other attributes
Selection for improved productivity—whether applied amongst a group of milking cows or amongst tested bulls

standing in an AI stud—differs both qualitatively and conceptually from selection for all other attributes.

Whereas the increased revenues obtained in response to selection for productivity contribute directly and unequivocally to the primary objective of most milk producers, the same cannot be said of the many other attributes that influence the selection and usage of bulls in dairy herds. For those concerned primarily with profit maximisation and business efficiency, *any* selection for animal form and type, behaviour and temperament, calving and milking characteristics can only be sustained and justified *either* on the grounds that the practice contributes to lifetime performance by raising the survival prospects of the more desirable offspring *or* against the admission that other objectives (e.g. aesthetics and convenience) cannot be ignored even at the ultimate expense of profits.

Consequently, the degree of unanimity exhibited and expressed by producers in their recognition of productivity as an important criterion of selection tends to be eroded by the extent to which they differ in their need or willingness to compromise their primary aim to accommodate other goals.

3. Daughter type

Bearing in mind (a) that the tested bulls initially available for selection by farmers have already been screened by testing organisations and the worst offenders removed, (b) that a high production rating already offers a useful assurance concerning functional merit and survival prospects, (c) that female culling within the herd provides opportunities at a later date to weed out undesirable animal types, and (d) that the inclusion of other attributes must diminish selection pressure for the primary objective (see Figure 11), the vexed and contentious question as to whether a direct preference for daughter type can be justified when choosing bulls for use in the herd and, if so, to what extent, can still only be answered on pragmatic grounds.

The importance to the farmer of the functional components of animal form is clearly reflected in the rapidity with which seriously defective material is expelled from his herd. Though this observation seems to confirm that the first criterion for including daughter type in the selection programme—i.e. its importance in the scale of priorities—is fulfilled, it is by no means firmly established that selective breeding within herds is either an appropriate or an effective treatment in this case.

Differences between type classification schemes and classifiers, further complicated by herd, age, season, special treatment and cosmetic culling effects that cannot be corrected or removed by statistical means, have combined to create a situation in which it is still legitimate and necessary to question whether variation in type scores between bulls reflects biological and genetic values sufficiently precisely for use by individuals seeking long-term improvements in functional merit.

The evidence obtained from herds that have consistently ignored type selection and suffered no demonstrable deterioration in type status and of breeding programmes that have sought improvement by selective breeding with erratic and inconsistent consequences tends to point in the opposite direction. Consequently, despite the importance of the utility traits and a natural disinclination to ignore type scores in sire selection, lack of precision and discriminatory power in the descriptive processes by which variation in type status is communicated to others renders the information of dubious value in selective breeding. Recently introduced linear type scoring methods, which seek to differentiate between the aesthetic and utility components of type, may help to resolve some of these difficulties but as yet have not been shown to do so.

Thus, in present circumstances and for the reasons stated, it would seem that any direct selection amongst proven bulls that amounts to anything more than a rejection of the extreme deviants in the functional attributes can only be practised at the immediate expense of herd performance and profits. Whilst a single-minded pursuit of type excellence may succeed in inducing genetic improvements in daughter type, the cost of this in terms of neglected selection for productivity is likely to prove exorbitant, more than offsetting the financial benefits obtained.

Simultaneous selection for a combination of daughter performance and daughter type poses other difficulties in attempting to reconcile two qualitatively different—and, hence, essentially irreconcilable—sets of selection criteria. Whereas differences between sire progeny groups in the primary production traits—milk yield and compositional quality—are based on entirely objective measurements of volume, weight and content that can be assigned meaningful monetary values that differ little from one producer to the next, type scores are entirely subjective, impossible to quantify in monetary values and of varying importance to each individual farmer.

Consequently, the index selection methods that normally offer a solution to the problem of optimising simultaneous selection for several attributes are precluded in this instance by the impossibility of assigning meaningful weights to each component of the type-production complex. Index procedures that have been applied for this purpose—for example, in the USA—have not resolved this basic problem but have merely bypassed it by assigning arbitrary values arrived at by consensus. Sire assessments based on these procedures, if not entirely misleading, do not necessarily reflect the varied priorities and needs of individual producers and may conceal deficiencies in some components of the index.

In the absence of effective and versatile index selection methods, traditional independent culling methods still seem to offer a satisfactory solution in circumstances in which only relatively large differences between bulls are of interest and relevance to users of AI services. The procedure, which involves the specification of lower selection limits for the secondary traits followed by unconditional selection for the primary characteristic, is no less arbitrary than other processes but possesses the virtues of simplicity, versatility and efficacy. Provided that realistic and consistent standards are applied, the final outcome of the selection process is a group of bulls from which the extreme deviants in daughter type have been precluded and amongst which all subsequent selection is directed specifically towards the primary production traits.

The difficulties and anomalies encountered in attempting to rationalise selection for performance and daughter type are experienced in even more acute form in respect of the behavioural traits. Even though genetic variation in temperament, feeding habits and milking characteristics may be detectable within herds and apparent in resemblances between members of families, the ability of conventional recording and documentation processes to measure and communicate the nature and extent of differences in the behaviour of sire progeny groups dispersed throughout many herds is severely limited. For this reason, the prospects of discriminating between bulls standing at AI with any degree of consistency and reliability are remote indeed.

Negative, dismissive and unhelpful as these conclusions may be, they do reflect the reality of the present cattle breeding scene. If traits other than daughter productivity are to be included in the sire selection process then testing and recording methods more comprehensive and precise than those currently employed will have to be introduced. In the meantime, little useful purpose can be served by seeking to attain the unattainable however desirable it may appear to be.

Chapter 8

IMPLEMENTATION OF BREEDING PROGRAMMES

AT SEVERAL points throughout the text it has been suggested that the breeding of a highly productive and profitable dairy herd, if slow and unmelodramatic, is nevertheless an entirely straightforward and rewarding process for anyone prepared to invest time and effort in the pursuit of this particular objective. Having examined the important factors that determine genetic change between generations and identified many points at which the individual may intervene to beneficial or detrimental effect, it now remains to attempt to draw all the various strands together in the form of a generalised breeding strategy for the commercial dairy herd.

After many years of trial and error, the processes by which most major development programmes are now planned and executed have assumed a standard form. Whilst remembering that the conduct of the dairy herd business differs fundamentally from most other industrial processes in dealing with biological material subject to natural forces, the disciplined methods of project planning and execution may still be enlisted to beneficial effect.

FORMULATING THE BLUEPRINT

Since the many and varied objectives of most dairy farmers are not always abundantly clear either to themselves or to those whose responsibility it may be to advise and assist them, the discipline involving in defining clear objectives, in examining and appraising the various treatments applied to the herd and in cataloguing the resources available can itself prove illuminating and highly rewarding. Even if the basic studies fail to identify any pressing need for new initiatives or for radical changes of emphasis and direction, new opportunities and misplaced efforts are frequently revealed.

For those embarking on a career in commercial milk production and wishing to include selective breeding amongst their herd treatments, and for anyone seeking to introduce an effective programme to a herd in which selective breeding may have been neglected in the past, the primary objective may be stated in simple terms—namely, the highest attainable profit commensurate with animal welfare interests and other conditioning wishes of the owner. If the vigour with which these secondary aims are pursued alongside the primary objective remains entirely at the discretion of the herd owner, their presence ought at least to be justified on the basis of a knowledge of the magnitude and nature of the unseen costs incurred by way of other opportunities foregone. Once again, this can only be accomplished by means of a rigorous initial accounting exercise.

The most productive, profitable and satisfying dairy herd may be defined as one in which all useful treatments are competently applied and which contains the highest proportion of animals that conform to the ultimate concept of total merit. At the present time, the best and only dispassionate guide to total merit is the genetic index rating of the individual cow and the mean genetic rating of the herd.

Whilst acknowledging that genetic index ratings may not provide a complete or ultimate assessment of animal merit and still need to be further refined, no other source of information can be depended upon to produce an equally consistent response to selective breeding. Accordingly, the acquisition of a herd characterised by a high genetic index rating constitutes an objective that can be confidently recommended and widely applied, that will ensure high productivity and profitability and which possesses the added virtues of simplicity and singularity of purpose. In contrast to the ill-defined and sometimes contradictory objectives of many breeders, the components that contribute to this particular aim can be clearly identified, are well documented and studied and are also mutually compatible. Further, the operational processes by which to achieve high index ratings are simple and dependable.

High genetic index ratings can be attained only when a parentage of proven genetic excellence is combined with high individual merit expressed over several lactation periods. This particular combination of circumstances is present in fullest measure only amongst the more productive daughters and granddaughters of the better proven sires and maternal grandsires. Offspring of moderate parents, however meritorious they may seem to be on the strength of their own performance records, rarely attain a high genetic rating (Table 17). Since the proven males that tend to dominate the index estimates have been stringently tested throughout many herds, considerable protection is provided against the misleading effects of special treatments of the kind that inflate the performance and apparent merit of individual females.

Seen in this context and interpreted in this manner, the much maligned and misunderstood cow index—seen earlier to be of marginal value when used for purposes of cow culling and selection—emerges with great credit as an important objective highly desirable in its own right. Whilst its incompleteness as a measure of total merit has been seized on in the past to support an alleged need for other aids to selection (e.g. intuition, the breeder's 'eye' for a superior animal), this argument presupposes that these other processes are able to supply what an index estimate cannot. However, to the extent that the inadequacies of the index relate essentially to its neglect of characteristics that are either intrinsically unsuitable for inclusion in a breeding programme anyway, or else to its neglect of attributes that can be satisfactorily controlled by corrective culling within the herd, the case for employing other supplementary procedures cannot withstand serious scrutiny.

Once the primary objective has been identified and agreed, the problem is reduced to one of defining ways and means by which to achieve it most rapidly and effectively with the resources already available or obtainable from other sources.

At the crucial time that mating decisions are taken, only the parental component of the index is open to manipulation by the breeder. At this time, the paternal and maternal contributions can be maximised only in herds in which the

Table 17. Example of a typical herd index for milk yield

Number of lactations	Cow	Dam	Milk yield (kg) MHS*	PHS†	Daughters	Index value (kg)	Accuracy (repeatability)
7	+ 89	—	—	− 354	+ 866	− 13	0.77
7	+ 410	+ 620	+ 935	+ 76	+ 93	+ 311	0.77
6	+1,865	+2,432	+1,773	—	− 4	+1,113	0.75
6	+ 715	—	—	− 277	+ 124	+ 236	0.78
6	+ 339	+ 336	+ 749	+ 165	+ 219	+ 318	0.79
6	+ 240	+ 111	—	+ 160	− 110	− 60	0.76
5	− 333	+1,057	+1,062	+ 96	—	+ 105	0.77
5	+1,521	+1,140	—	+ 186	—	+ 840	0.76
4	+ 306	+ 306	—	− 126	− 108	+ 80	0.76
4	+ 72	+1,107	—	+ 479	+ 265	+ 220	0.73
4	−1,588	−1,257	—	+ 215	—	− 883	0.75
3	+ 703	+ 797	+ 400	− 9	—	− 120	0.73
2	+ 758	+ 47	—	+ 39	—	+ 242	0.70
2	− 189	+1,414	+ 532	− 277	—	+ 131	0.67
1	+1,272	+ 967	—	− 689	—	+ 127	0.63
1	+ 71	− 729	—	− 767	—	− 602	0.66
1	+ 630	+ 857	—	+ 387	—	+ 570	0.66

*MHS = Maternal half-sisters.
†PHS = Paternal half-sisters = the progeny test of the sire.

most highly rated proven sires available are consistently and repeatedly used in matings with daughters and granddaughters of equally highly rated bulls of previous generations. Though the planning of such matings may present few logistic problems in herds in which the leading proven bulls have been used for many years, in other cases a large maternal contribution to the index can only be achieved either by acquiring suitable females from other herds or else by processes of accumulation over many years.

Within this clearly defined strategy for herd improvement, it will be noted that the achievement of the ultimate objective is most sensitive of all to the efficiency with which the males are selected and used—both as mates of cows and as sires and grandsires of subsequent female generations. Any weakness in male usage is likely to reveal itself very clearly in subsequent index estimates and may be precluded before any matings take place. Those who assign their sire selection priorities correctly and consistently will witness the benefits of this not only in increased milk sales but also in the elevated status of the index values. Those who fail to do so, whilst not more badly placed than before, at least have the index estimates available by which to diagnose the main reasons for failure. Within this scenario, the females are utilised not to actively promote herd improvement—a function for which they are ill suited—but rather to cleanse the herd of undesirable traits of secondary importance introduced by the bulls.

EXECUTION

The introduction and implementation of a planned breeding programme may be accomplished slowly and tentatively by progressive replacement of inadequate male and female parents by superior progeny or, more immediately, by more drastic treatments applied to an existing herd. In the latter case, a more rapid and complete approach to the ultimate objective is achieved but at an increased immediate cost in terms of female disposal and replacement.

Where an extensive range of AI proven sires is available to choose from, the replacement of any males or semen used previously can be accomplished overnight merely by a change in sire selection policy. The only cost incurred is that of disposing of unwanted semen or stock bulls and the only effort entailed that of ensuring that the sire selection criteria applied henceforth are fully competent to ensure the achievement of a large positive paternal contribution to the herd index. Once the sire selection methods have been established, the same basic pattern of sire usage proceeds routinely from year to year, with proven sires used repeatedly on daughters and granddaughters of other superior proven bulls and replaced only whenever superior males become available.

Continuous use of the male sex in this fashion is entirely sufficient in itself to ensure the eventual emergence of a highly productive herd characterised by a high genetic index rating. However, if genetic improvement is promoted solely through the males, several female generations may need to pass through the herd before it contains a high proportion of females of the highest genetic calibre. This protracted process, which may span 15–20 years, can be foreshortened by the use of embryo transfer, by the introduction of suitable female stock from other sources and also by an initial reorganisation of the structure and age composition of the herd to ensure that current and subsequent female culling and replacement procedures are applied to best advantage.

A dairy herd in which regular routine culling has been conscientiously and effectively applied to animals of all ages and in which a balance has been maintained between the pursuit of long- and short-term aims tends to display a distinctive age structure and shape (Figure 24). Such herds differ from recently established units and from herds in which great emphasis has been laid upon immediate objectives, in containing a relatively high proportion of older cows. Herds in which milking cows and young stock are disposed of merely whenever an urgent need arises or an immediate profit can be realised tend to divulge the absence of budgeting and forward planning in the form of a grossly distorted or abnormal age structure.

Those wishing to upgrade the genetic status of a neglected herd rapidly and at relatively low cost may do so by

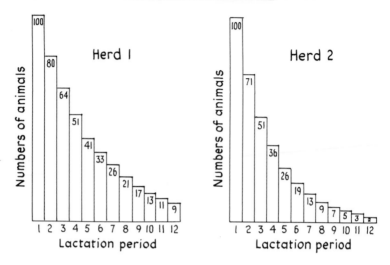

Fig. 24. The effect of differential culling rates on the proportion of animals surviving to different ages.

maximising all opportunities to introduce genetically superior young stock at the earliest time. Initially, this entails the retention of a high proportion of the calves and young heifers and the heavy culling of older animals to create space for them. Once the initial establishment process has been completed, the female culling and replacement procedure tends to assume a stable form which permits a regular and rapid flow of replacements into the milking herd. Having attained this level of stability, the forward planning of semen requirements and the construction of timetables depicting the flow of animals into and out of the herd can be accomplished with a considerable degree of precision.

LONG-TERM CONSEQUENCES

The products of a first-rate selective breeding programme engender several interesting, important and possibly unforeseen consequences for the owners of dairy herds, for those who supply them with goods and services and for those who depend on them for raw materials.

Dairy herds that contain a high proportion of genetically superior milking animals and young stock rapidly become highly self-sufficient and self-contained. In circumstances in which few suppliers are able to offer stock genetically superior to that which the herd is able to propagate to its own specification from its own resources and in which the asset value and productivity of individual animals precludes the taking of any unnecessary risk of introducing disease, external sources of supply rapidly lose their attraction and potential value. The implications of this for specialised breeders, tending to pursue aims which differ from those of their commercial customers and able to thrive only where others have neglected the development of their own animal resources, are obvious, serious and potentially terminal.

Within the herd itself, the emergence of animals of high genetic merit immediately highlights weaknesses in other aspects of herd management and provides attractive new incentives to attend to them. Consequently, a herd development programme originally viewed and designated as an exercise primarily in animal breeding rapidly ceases to be such as soon as the initial genetic constraint is raised or removed. At this point, every other major aspect and component of herd management and animal treatment has to be clinically re-examined and corrected where seen to inhibit animal performance.

In drawing attention to other weaknesses in general herd management and in providing attractive incentives to correct them, a sound and progressive breeding programme possibly makes its largest, unrecognised, contribution to dairy herd improvement.

THE FUTURE

If the past can be held directly responsible for imposing many of the constraints within which farmers now conduct their business, the future poses a threat, an opportunity and a source of profound uncertainty.

For an enterprise dependent on raw materials that entail a 3–5 year manufacturing process and may have to be utilised for 10–15 years thereafter, anticipation of the future and the manipulation of resources in preparation for it are necessary and potentially rewarding activities. In circumstances in which markets are constantly changing in response to many long- and short-term influences, in which materials and methods are responding to technical innovation and improved understanding and in which primary products have to compete in the market place with alternatives offered by others, neglect can rapidly engender inadequate raw materials and products no longer appropriate to consumer needs.

The forecasting process employs two basic techniques—the extrapolation of past and present trends into the future and the identification and evaluation of innovative techniques. The former involves discrimination between trends that are likely to continue, intensify, diminish or cease altogether, the latter an ability to discriminate between the useful and practical as opposed to the plausible but unusable products of the technologist and innovator.

1. Interpretation of trends

Amongst the daily, monthly, seasonal and annual fluctuations and cycles that tend to characterise and complicate all aspects of the farming business, several important and persistent influences can be identified as being responsible for many of the major changes that distinguish dairy farming in the 1980s from that of earlier decades.

The typical production unit of today differs from its predecessors in being larger and more productive, in containing bigger animals of a different breed type, in deriving a higher proportion of its revenue from milk sold for manufacturing purposes and in utilising AI, exotic sources of breeding stock and specialist support and technical aids to a greater extent than ever before. Throughout the entire Developed World, pressure exerted by conservation and animal welfare interests has steadily increased, imposing further constraints on freedom of choice and action.

In contemplating the major changes that have occurred in the past two or three decades, it is difficult to envisage an end to any of them or to clearly identify any specific development that is likely to interrupt, diminish or reverse them. Once firmly established, such influences tend to develop a momentum of their own and to persist long after the need for them has been removed. This being the case, the most probable form of the dairy industry in the 1990s and beyond would seem to be one containing very large specialised production units selling milk solids, mainly in the form of milk protein, for manufacturing purposes. This material is likely to emanate from animal populations mainly of purebred Holstein type supplying a beef by-product from surplus calves and cull cows. Whether or not the dairy farming business will continue to be conducted by private enterprise in the form of farmer–owners remains to be seen, though the trends in herd size and in the capital investment and skills needed to establish a dairy unit and sustain it thereafter would all seem to point in the direction of some other form of executive control in the future.

Unfortunately, the centralised marketing arrangements that have served producers so well in the past do not appear to have adapted and developed rapidly enough in response to social, political and structural changes of recent decades. In the presence of adequate marketing and trading arrangements the costly and counterproductive surpluses of the present time could have been avoided, to the benefit of agriculture and society in general. If balanced demand and supply patterns are to be re-established and former levels of income stability and security restored, the creation of effective integrated marketing schemes within Western Europe and beyond will be needed. Whilst the foundation processes may engender an initial period of disruption, reorganisation and uncertainty, and encounter producer hostility on that account, the long-term benefits to producers and consumers alike are likely to exceed those that followed the introduction of national marketing schemes half a century ago.

Until now, extensive breeding systems based on the field testing of dairy bulls have sufficed to meet a high priority need for improved animal productivity, efficiency and profitability. However, their very considerable success in this direction has itself highlighted the inhibiting and debilitating effects of low fertility, disease susceptibility and unsatisfactory

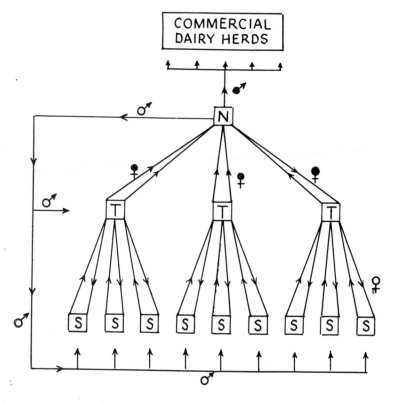

Fig. 25. *Schematic illustration of a group breeding scheme for dairy cattle improvement.*

behaviour—thereby engendering a widespread need and demand for breeding systems and documentation processes sufficiently flexible, comprehensive and precise to provide useful information on all aspects of animal performance.

Co-operative breeding schemes of the kind now employed to improve the genetic merit of sheep and beef cattle stocks in

Australasia (Figure 25) would appear to be entirely suitable for this purpose and seem likely to make an appearance in dairy cattle breeding in the foreseeable future as dairy herds continue to increase in size and as the needs of dairy farmers increase in complexity and sophistication. Unlike most other innovations in dairy cattle breeding which tend to be promoted from above, this particular development would seem to be eminently suitable for adoption by groups of individuals.

The haphazard processes by which transfers and exchanges of breeding material between countries and continents have occurred in the past, as and when a specific need or an occasional opportunity has arisen, appear ready to assume a more rational, organised and planned form and structure in the future. The need for regular and guaranteed supplies of the best raw materials available and the benefits that this would confer are similar in nature to those that prompted the formulation of centralised marketing arrangements in the 1930s and ensured their subsequent success. The scale benefits and vast financial rewards awaiting those first able to fully exploit the genetic value of superior parental stock at international and global level would appear sufficient in themselves to engender solutions to the immediate practical problems posed by disease and potentially hostile local vested interests. Whilst dairy farmers may not participate actively in this development on their own account, they stand to benefit from it by virtue of the wider choice of better breeding material made available to them.

2. Developments in technology

At an earlier point in the text it was concluded that the low natural fecundity of the female still constitutes the most important single obstacle standing in the way of dairy herd improvement. A technical breakthrough with respect to the reproductive capacity of the dairy cow, of the kind that has permitted the males to generate offspring in hundreds and thousands, will immediately raise the status and genetic potential of the female sex to the same level as that of the male, will place dairy cattle on essentially the same level as pigs and poultry for selective breeding purposes and will provoke far-reaching changes in operational procedures within the herd itself.

Whilst the recently introduced commercial embryo transfer services represent a first hesitant step in this direction, the high cost of the service and its unreliability place it out of reach of most commercial dairy farmers at the present time. In the foreseeable future, the facility to produce clusters of offspring of the same sex from a single embryo, to predetermine the sex of natural offspring and to induce multiple births as and when required may be anticipated.

These techniques, all involving interference with natural reproductive events, not only affect the numbers of offspring obtained from the more desirable parents but also the type of animal used to complete the gestation phase and the timing of birth and lactation processes. Ultimately, these latter possibilities may prove of greater value and significance to producers than the facility to reproduce large numbers of offspring to order.

For all milk producers, the ability to propagate offspring of the required number and sex at the most opportune time, and to do so utilising non-productive surrogate 'mothers', opens up an entirely novel range of possibilities and opportunities. In the first place, the timing and co-ordination of milk outputs may be predetermined to suit the convenience of producers and to optimise revenues from milk sales to a degree not previously attainable. Further, the opportunity afforded by the same techniques to dissociate the propagation and rearing processes from the milk production processes will permit the application of highly developed skills to these very different disciplines, thereby introducing another level of specialisation.

Against this background, the emergence of dairy herds containing productive animals only, and deriving their supply of high-quality female replacements from specialised rearing units fulfilling this sole function, is neither difficult to envisage nor lacking in plausibility. The further possibilities that this prospect opens up for the introduction of improved testing and monitoring of animal performance are intriguing and endless.

In the more distant future, the genetic engineering

techniques presently being tested and developed in laboratories may offer the primary producer animal stocks of a specification impossible to envisage in the light of current knowledge and experience. Whilst it is idle to speculate at the present time on the many possible consequences that may flow from this, it is probable that many of the apparently intractable problems associated with animal disease and other forms of wastage and loss that have so far escaped the competence of the breeder to resolve will eventually succumb to treatments supplied by the technologist.

Confronted by prospects of this kind, it has to be recognised that many of the routine techniques available to stockmen for several decades have never been employed to full effect for fear of the damaging consequences that could ensue. The AI technique itself, possessed of a power to induce genetic change in dairy cattle populations far beyond anything that has been witnessed or experienced so far, still awaits full exploitation. Quite apart from consumer preferences of the kind that cause many more bulls to be used through AI than are needed to perpetuate dairy herds, the heavy usage of a small number of superior sires has been resisted in the past on account of uncertainties as to their total suitability. Once again, inadequate testing and monitoring is seen to impose a major restriction on the utilisation of technology, a constraint that will apply even more forcibly in the future. Whatever exciting and novel prospects may emerge with the passage of time, improved utilisation of existing techniques still affords very large opportunities for further advancement.

In the male sex, the most important problem still confronting the technologist is the long-standing one of identifying genetic superiority in the young animal. Whilst the facility to do so may be superficially attractive in obviating or diminishing the need for costly and protracted progeny testing processes, all the trends identified earlier would seem to point to a need for greater accuracy in male selection and increased usage of the proven bulls. This being so, the prospects of obtaining indirect estimates of genetic merit comparable in accuracy with the direct assessments obtained from daughter groups are remote indeed. Even when used merely as initial screening devices to pinpoint the most promising candidates for testing, indirect assessments have failed so far to add anything of value to the information obtainable by pedigree analysis and projection.

3. Ultimate limits to animal improvement

For how much longer will animals continue to respond to selective breeding and other herd treatments and what levels of productivity may they ultimately attain? These, and other speculative questions of similar kind, whilst of some passing academic interest, presuppose that the innate capacity of animals to respond to treatments and man's own ability to continue to devise more effective treatments in the future must be finite. There is no *a priori* reason for believing this to be the case.

The diminishing response syndrome appears to characterise all business ventures sooner or later. To this extent, the attainment of ultimate limits seems inevitable. It has to be noted, however, that this self-fulfilling prophecy applies *only to the exhaustion of possibilities arising from the application of current methods to existing resources.* The introduction of novel methods and materials and of new personnel to a business may introduce in turn an entirely new range of improved prospects for the future, thereby establishing new response curves at higher levels than before and postponing, if not entirely eliminating, the attainment of final limits (Figure 26). Whilst individual businesses may succumb to exhaustion, those that replace them tend to commence business at a higher starting point possessed of many advantages either not available to those they replace or not fully utilised by them.

Consequently, the argument concerning the approach to ultimate limits in dairy cattle improvement applies only in circumstances in which all current possibilities are fully exploited (i.e. all treatments operate at optimal levels of efficiency) and in which all possibilities of further improvement by innovation are exhausted.

In practice, the processes by which exhaustion occurs and limits are reached may be witnessed in herds that have failed to maintain a steady and consistent improvement in

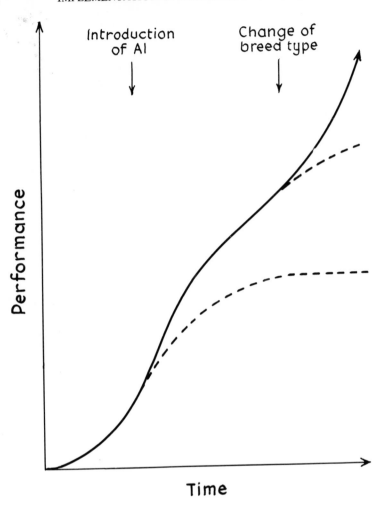

Fig. 26. The effect of innovation on long-term responses to selective breeding.

performance and in breeds that have failed to sustain a competitive status. The processes by which rejuvenation and reinvigoration occur and new response possibilities are introduced are well illustrated by the impact that AI has had on previously moribund cattle populations and by the influence of Holstein breeding material on European dairy cattle stocks.

Even in the absence of further major developments of this order of magnitude, full and efficient exploitation of present possibilities—including the removal of the anomalies that hinder the development of neglected animal populations in the developing world—will ensure that the productivity of the *typical* dairy cow of the future will match that of the *most productive* members of today's stock. For most, this prospect alone provides a sufficient challenge and incentive to continue.

INDEX

(Main entries in **bold** type)